Challenge

Maths

KS2: Year 5 Age 9–10
Paul Broadbent and
Peter Patilla

Hachette UK's policy is to use papers that are natural, renewable and recyclable products and made from wood grown in sustainable forests. The logging and manufacturing processes are expected to conform to the environmental regulations of the country of origin.

Orders: please contact Bookpoint Ltd, 130 Milton Park, Abingdon, Oxon OX14 4SB. Telephone: +44 (0)1235 827720. Fax: +44 (0)1235 400454. Lines are open 9.00a.m.–5.00p.m., Monday to Saturday, with a 24-hour message answering service. Visit our website at www.hoddereducation.co.uk.

© Paul Broadbent and Peter Patilla 2013
First published in 2007 exclusively for WHSmith by
Hodder Education
An Hachette UK Company
338 Euston Road
London NW1 3BH

This revised edition first published 2013
Teacher's tips © Matt Koster 2013
Impression number   10 9 8 7 6 5 4 3 2
Year   2018 2017 2016 2015 2014 2013

Cover illustration by Oxford Designers and Illustrators Ltd
Illustrations © Hodder Education
Typeset in Folio Book 14pt by DC Graphic Design Ltd
Printed in Italy

A catalogue record for this title is available from the British Library

ISBN 978 1444 188 370

Conte

Parents' notes

How this book can help your child

- This book has been written for children who are between 9 and 10 years old.

- It will support and improve the work they are doing at school, whichever Maths scheme they use.

- The activities in the book have been carefully written to include the content expected of children at this stage in their development.

- The activities will help prepare your child for all types of tests.

Materials needed

- Pencil, eraser, watch and centimetre ruler.

Using this book

- There are 24 topics and 4 tests in the book. Each test covers 6 topics.

- Each topic is about a week's work.

- Do give help and encouragement. The activities should be fun!

- A calculator should not be used for the work in this book.

- Do let your child mark his or her own work under your supervision and correct any careless mistakes he or she might have made.

- When all the tests have been completed let your child fill in the Certificate of Achievement on the opposite page

- Each double page has a title, explanation of the learning point, practice section, and challenge section.

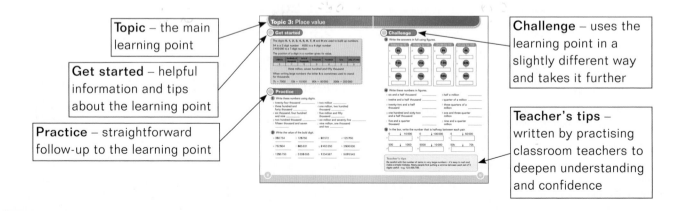

Topic – the main learning point

Get started – helpful information and tips about the learning point

Practice – straightforward follow-up to the learning point

Challenge – uses the learning point in a slightly different way and takes it further

Teacher's tips – written by practising classroom teachers to deepen understanding and confidence

This certifies
that

_____

has completed

CHALLENGE MATHS YEAR 5

on _____

Scoring _____ on TEST 1

_____ on TEST 2

_____ on TEST 3

and _____ on TEST 4

Total score
out of 100 _____ 40–49   good effort
50–59   well done
60–69   fantastic
70–100 brilliant

Topic 1: Mental maths

Get started

You should be able to work out addition and subtraction facts quickly in your head. Some of these facts may help you.

To add or subtract numbers ending in 9 use the next tens number then adjust the answer by adding or subtracting 1.

$226 + 9$ (add 10 then subtract 1) = 235
$547 + 39$ (add 40 then subtract 1) = 586
$678 - 99$ (subtract 100 then add 1) = 579
$678 - 99$ (subtract 100 then add 1) = 579
$872 - 19$ (subtract 20 then add 1) = 853

If there are brackets always work out this part first.

$24 + (\mathbf{17 - 5}) =$
$24 + \mathbf{12} = 36$

$50 - (\mathbf{14 + 6}) =$
$50 - \mathbf{20} = 30$

Practice

1 Try to answer each block as quickly as you can.

a
$8 + 7 = 15$
$17 - 9 = 8$
$9 + 9 = 18$
$15 - 7 = 8$
$12 + 6 = 18$
$20 - 7 = 13$
$5 + 8 = 13$
$11 - 5 = 6$

b
$14 + 7 = 21$
$36 - 9 = 27$
$55 + 9 = 64$
$71 - 7 = 64$
$65 + 6 = 71$
$80 - 7 = 73$
$75 + 8 = 83$
$41 - 5 = 36$

c
$30 + 50 = 80$
$70 + 70 = 140$
$20 + 60 = 80$
$50 + 50 = 100$
$90 + 60 = 150$
$30 + 60 = 90$
$80 + 80 = 170$
$70 + 40 = 110$

d
$67 + 9 = 76$
$73 + 9 = 82$
$99 + 9 = 108$
$75 + 9 = 84$
$64 + 9 = 73$
$87 - 9 = 78$
$72 - 9 = 63$
$64 - 9 = 55$

e
$267 + 99 = 366$
$573 + 99 = 672$
$699 + 99 = 798$
$475 + 99 = 574$
$864 + 99 = 963$
$787 - 99 = 688$
$472 - 99 = 373$
$864 - 99 = 865$

2 Work the answers out in your head.

a
$67 + 19 = 86$
$56 + 39 = 95$
$77 + 59 = 136$
$38 + 99 = 137$

b
$72 + 69 = 141$
$127 + 19 = 146$
$307 + 49 = 346$
$338 + 29 = 367$

c
$267 + 99 = 366$
$638 + 59 = 697$
$82 - 19 = 63$
$56 - 29 = 27$

d
$85 - 49 = 36$
$56 - 39 = 17$
$86 - 59 = \underline{\hspace{1cm}}$
$256 - 29 = \underline{\hspace{1cm}}$

3 Try to work these out in your head.

a
$72 - (8 + 7) = \underline{\hspace{1cm}}$
$80 - (12 + 5) = \underline{\hspace{1cm}}$
$55 - (16 + 4) = \underline{\hspace{1cm}}$

b
$90 - (18 - 9) = \underline{\hspace{1cm}}$
$85 - (20 - 6) = \underline{\hspace{1cm}}$
$72 - (17 - 9) = \underline{\hspace{1cm}}$

c
$38 + (12 - 5) = \underline{\hspace{1cm}}$
$45 + (19 - 8) = \underline{\hspace{1cm}}$
$76 + (13 - 8) = \underline{\hspace{1cm}}$

d
$45 + (12 + 8) = \underline{\hspace{1cm}}$
$59 + (15 + 4) = \underline{\hspace{1cm}}$
$64 + (16 + 3) = \underline{\hspace{1cm}}$

4 Write in the missing numbers. Both sides of the balance must have the same answer.

a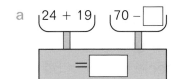

b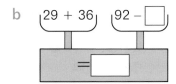

c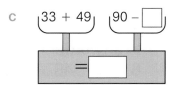

d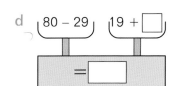

e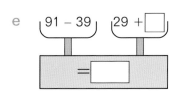

f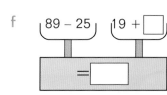

g 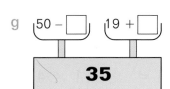   **35**

h 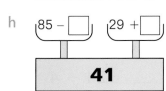   **41**

i 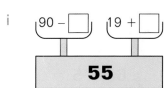   **55**

5 Complete the tables.

a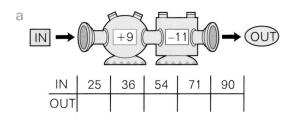

IN	25	36	54	71	90
OUT					

b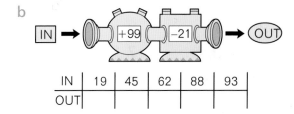

IN	19	45	62	88	93
OUT					

c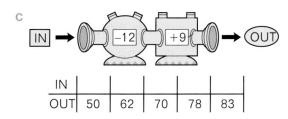

IN					
OUT	50	62	70	78	83

d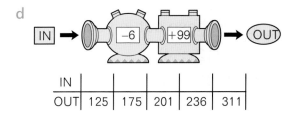

IN					
OUT	125	175	201	236	311

6 Draw brackets to make each number sentence true.

a $16 - 4 + 6 = 6$ b $20 - 9 + 4 = 15$ c $17 - 3 + 7 = 21$ d $22 - 9 + 1 = 12$

e $13 - 7 - 2 = 8$ f $18 - 10 - 3 = 11$ g $20 - 8 - 4 = 8$ h $21 - 10 - 3 = 8$

Teacher's tips

Look for patterns or approximations that make problems easier to solve. If there are two parts, write the answer you have solved first to help you solve the second part.

Topic 2: Tables

Get started

You should be able to work out multiplication and division tables quickly in your head. Some of these facts may help you.

You can multiply in any order:	Doubling can help you:	Check ÷ by ×
$6 \times 8 = 48$	$7 \times \mathbf{3} = 21$ so $7 \times \mathbf{6} = 42$	$54 \div 9 = 6$
$8 \times 6 = 48$	and $7 \times \mathbf{12} = 84$	Check: $6 \times 9 = 54$
	$9 \times \mathbf{2} = 18$ so $9 \times \mathbf{4} = 36$	$42 \div 7 = 6$
	and $9 \times \mathbf{8} = 72$	Check: $6 \times 7 = 42$

Practice

1 Try to answer each block as quickly as you can.

a
$6 \times 5 =$ __
$7 \times 7 =$ __
$9 \times 8 = 1$
$4 \times 3 =$ __
$7 \times 3 =$ __
$9 \times 5 = 45$
$4 \times 10 =$ __
$0 \times 6 =$ __

b
$6 \times 6 =$ __
$9 \times 6 =$ __
$8 \times 9 = 72$
$10 \times 8 =$ __
$9 \times 2 = 18$
$8 \times 6 =$ __
$7 \times 4 =$ __
$8 \times 4 =$ __

c
$24 \div 4 =$ __
$30 \div 6 =$ __
$54 \div 9 =$ __
$36 \div 9 =$ __
$45 \div 9 =$ __
$40 \div 8 =$ __
$35 \div 5 =$ __
$21 \div 3 =$ __

d
$28 \div 4 =$ __
$42 \div 6 =$ __
$27 \div 9 =$ __
$48 \div 8 =$ __
$49 \div 7 =$ __
$64 \div 8 =$ __
$15 \div 5 =$ __
$30 \div 3 =$ __

e
$11 \times 4 =$ ____
$11 \times 7 =$ ____
$11 \times 9 =$ ____
$11 \times 3 =$ ____
$11 \times 8 =$ ____
$12 \times 4 =$ ____
$12 \times 5 =$ ____
$12 \times 6 =$ ____

2 Work these out in your head. Remember to work out the brackets first.

a $3 \times (12 \div 4) =$ ____   b $7 \times (56 \div 8) =$ ____   c $5 \times (36 \div 4) =$ ____

d $54 \div (15 - 6) =$ ____   e $72 \div (17 - 9) =$ ____   f $40 \div (19 - 14) =$ ____

g $(6 \times 7) - 5 =$ ____   h $(7 \times 7) - 8 =$ ____   i $(6 \times 10) - 19 =$ ____

j $(36 \div 4) + 19 =$ ____   k $(81 \div 9) + 45 =$ ____   l $(42 \div 7) + 72 =$ ____

3 Complete these grids.

a

×	4	6	8
3			
7			
9			

b

×	3	5	8
9			
11			
12			

c

×			
4	12	20	36
6			
7			

d

×	3	5	9
		15	
		24	
		27	

Challenge

4 Write two different multiplications for each answer.

All four numbers you use must be different.

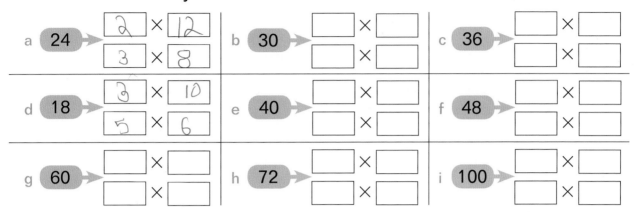

a 24 → [2] × [12]
         [3] × [8]

b 30 → [ ] × [ ]
        [ ] × [ ]

c 36 → [ ] × [ ]
        [ ] × [ ]

d 18 → [3] × [10]
        [5] × [6]

e 40 → [ ] × [ ]
        [ ] × [ ]

f 48 → [ ] × [ ]
        [ ] × [ ]

g 60 → [ ] × [ ]
        [ ] × [ ]

h 72 → [ ] × [ ]
        [ ] × [ ]

i 100 → [ ] × [ ]
         [ ] × [ ]

5 Answer these word problems.

Work out the answers in your head.

a One book costs £6.
What will seven books cost? _____

b Four tickets cost £24.
What would two tickets cost? _____

c One sticker costs 5p.
What will twelve stickers cost? _____

d Nine packets cost 72p.
What would three packets cost? _____

e One toy costs £8.
What will four toys cost? _____

f Eight stickers cost 48p.
What would nine stickers cost? _____

g One ticket costs £12.
What will six tickets cost? _____

h Five books cost £30.
What would twelve books cost? _____

6 Answer these number riddles.

a I double a number and then add 7. The answer is 25. What was my number? [ ]

b I halve a number then add on 7. The answer is 11. What was my number? [ ]

c I divide a number by 5 then subtract 2. The answer is 4. What was my number? [ ]

d I subtract 5 from a number then multiply it by 3. The answer is 9. What was my number? [ ]

Teacher's tips

Solve the riddles by working backwards through the story doing the opposite action. Be careful to do it in the right order, starting with the last action and doing the exact opposite action!

Topic 3: Place value

Get started

The digits **0, 1, 2, 3, 4, 5, 6, 7, 8** and **9** are used to build up numbers.

54 is a 2-digit number   4550 is a 4-digit number
3 450 000 is a 7-digit number.

The position of a digit in a number gives its value.

millions	hundreds of thousands	tens of thousands	thousands	hundreds	tens	units of ones
3	7	5	0	0	0	0

three million, seven hundred and fifty thousand

When writing large numbers the letter **k** is sometimes used to stand for thousands.

7k = 7000   15k = 15 000   80k = 80 000   200k = 200 000

Practice

1 Write these numbers using digits.

a twenty-four thousand _____   b two million _____
c three hundred and
   forty thousand _____   d one million, two hundred
                                     thousand _____
e six thousand, four hundred
   and nine _____   f five million and fifty
                              thousand _____
g two hundred thousand _____   h six million and seventy-five _____
i fifteen thousand and seven   j nine million, one thousand
   _____   and two _____

2 Write the value of the bold digit.

a 3**5**0 754   b 125**7**50   c **9**2 572   d 125 **7**50

_____   _____   _____   _____

e 752 **5**04   f **6**85 631   g **2** 453 250   h 3 **5**00 000

_____   _____   _____   _____

i 12**5**5 750   j 5 5**5**5 555   k **1**234 567   l 9 8**7**6 543

_____   _____   _____   _____

Challenge

3 Write the answers in full using figures.

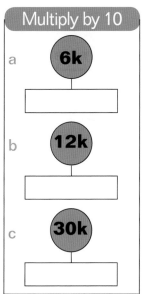
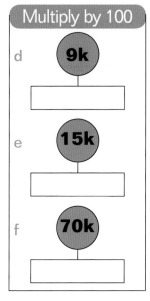
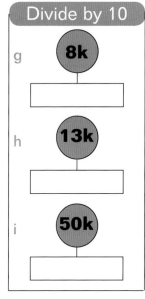
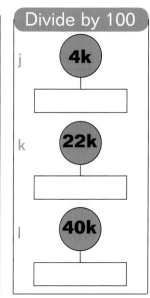

Multiply by 10	Multiply by 100	Divide by 10	Divide by 100
a **6k**	d **9k**	g **8k**	j **4k**
b **12k**	e **15k**	h **13k**	k **22k**
c **30k**	f **70k**	i **50k**	l **40k**

4 Write these numbers in figures.

a six and a half thousand _____

b half a million _____

c twelve and a half thousand _____

d quarter of a million _____

e twenty-two and a half thousand _____

f three-quarters of a million _____

g one hundred and sixty-two and a half thousand _____

h one and three-quarter million _____

i five and a quarter thousand _____

j nine and a quarter million _____

5 In the box, write the number that is halfway between each pair.

0	↓ 10 000	0	↓ 100 000	0	↓ 50 000
a		b		c	

500	↓ 1000	5000	↓ 10 000	50k	↓ 70k
d		e		f	

Teacher's tips

Be careful with the number of zeros in very large numbers – it's easy to rush and make a simple mistake. Many people find putting a comma between each set of 3 digits useful – e.g. 123,456,789.

Topic 4: Negative numbers

Get started

Negative numbers come before zero on a number line.

Positive numbers come after zero on a number line.

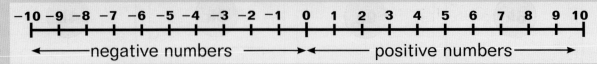

You say −5 as negative five or minus five.

Practice

1 To which number does the arrow point?

a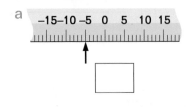

b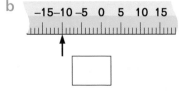

c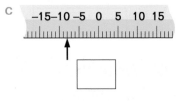

d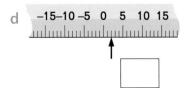

e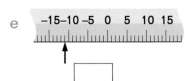

f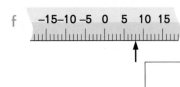

2 Write the missing numbers in these sequences.

a −5 −4 ☐ −2 −1 ☐ 1 2

b −10 −9 −8 ☐ ☐ −5 −4 −3

c −10 −8 −6 ☐ ☐ 0 2 4

d −12 −9 −6 ☐ ☐ 3 6 9

e −20 −16 ☐ −8 ☐ 0 4 8

f −50 ☐ −40 ☐ −30 −25 −20

3 Write these numbers in order, lowest number first.

a −5 −8 4 0 6

b 5 −9 −3 −1 4

_____

_____

c −20 −45 −50 10 0

d −32 25 17 − 67 −11

_____

_____

Challenge

4 Write the new temperatures.

a The temperature rises by 8°C. [ ]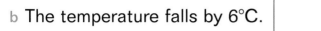

b The temperature falls by 6°C. [ ]

c The temperature falls by 7°C. [ ]

d The temperature rises by 4°C. [ ]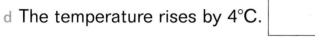

e The temperature rises by 6°C. [ ]

5 Write the answers.

a The temperature is 3°C and falls to −4°C.

By how many degrees has it dropped? [ ]

b The temperature is −9°C and goes up to 1°C.

By how many degrees has it risen? [ ]

c The temperature is −1°C and falls to −10°C.

By how many degrees has it dropped? [ ]

d The temperature is −5°C and goes up to 5°C.

By how many degrees has it risen? [ ]

e The temperature is −2°C and falls to −9°C.

By how many degrees has it dropped? [ ]

6 Write where you land on the number line.
Remember: move to the right when you add, move to the left
when you subtract.

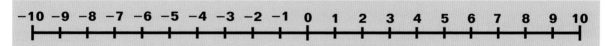

a 5 − 7 = [ ]   b 2 − 7 = [ ]   c 5 − 10 = [ ]   d 0 − 6 = [ ]

Teacher's tips

Use a number line with negative numbers in the same way as a regular number line,
but remember you must include zero as a 'jump/step'. Make your own number line,
which you can use at home.

Get started

The decimal point separates whole units from parts of units. Decimal points are used in numbers and measurements.

whole units **.** fractions of the unit

2 5 . 7 5 m

25 m and **75 cm**

Zeros are important when dealing with decimal points. Adding zeros does not always make the number bigger.

2.5   2.50   2.500
are worth the same
0.5   0.05   0.005
are not worth the same

The same measurement can be written in different ways:

$2\frac{1}{2}$ m = 2.5 m = 2.50 m = 2.500 m   1 m and 5 cm = 1.05 m
1 litre and 50 ml = 1.050 ml   1 litre and 5 ml = 1.005 ml
1 kg and 450 g = 1.450 kg = 1.45 kg

Practice

1 Write these measurements using a decimal point.

a 2 l and 700 ml = [   ] l   b 1 kg and 200 g = [   ] kg   c 2 km and 100 m = [   ] km

d 5 l and 50 ml = [   ] l   e 3 kg and 30 g = [   ] kg   f 1 km and 40 m = [   ] km

g 1 l and 5 ml = [   ] l   h 2 kg and 5 g = [   ] kg   i 5 km and 5 m = [   ] km

j 250 ml = [   ] l   k 750 g = [   ] kg   l 500 m = [   ] km

m $3\frac{1}{2}$ l = [   ] l   n $6\frac{1}{2}$ kg = [   ] kg   o $4\frac{1}{2}$ km = [   ] km

2 Complete these tables.

a

cm	m
280	
	5.5
307	
	0.2
600	

b

g	kg
1750	
	2.25
2075	
	0.8
750	

c

ml	l
2820	
	1.75
1075	
	0.2
900	

d

m	km
8500	
	3.25
5060	
	0.1
450	

Challenge

3 Write these measurements in order starting with the smallest.

a 450 g, $\frac{1}{2}$ kg, 0.405 kg ___ ___ ___   b $1\frac{1}{4}$ kg, 1.200 kg, 1025 g ___ ___ ___

c 2.705 kg, 2570 g, $2\frac{3}{4}$ kg ___ ___ ___   d $\frac{3}{4}$ kg, 800 g, 0.7 kg ___ ___ ___

e 700 ml, $\frac{3}{4}$ l, 0.705 l ___ ___ ___   f $1\frac{1}{4}$ l, 1215 ml, 1.125 l ___ ___ ___

g $2\frac{1}{4}$ l, 2.225 l, 2550 ml ___ ___ ___   h $1\frac{3}{4}$ l, 1.8 l, 1650 ml ___ ___ ___

4 Tick the most sensible measurement.

a
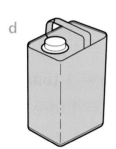
46 kg
4.600 kg
460 kg

b

0.200 kg
2 kg
20 kg

c
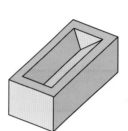
275 kg
2.750 kg
27 kg

d
5 l
500 l
50 l

e
50 ml
5 ml
500 ml

f
30 ml
3 l
0.3 l

5 Calculate the answers.

Write answers as kg	Write answers as l
a 450 g + 800 g + 900 g = [ ] kg	e 750 ml + 650 ml + 950 ml = [ ] l
b 2 kg − 250 g = [ ] kg	f 5 l − 125 ml = [ ] l
c $4\frac{1}{2}$ kg − 300 g = [ ] kg	g $2\frac{1}{2}$ l − 250 ml = [ ] l
d $1\frac{1}{2}$ kg + $1\frac{1}{4}$ kg = [ ] kg	h $3\frac{1}{2}$ l + $1\frac{1}{4}$ l = [ ] l

Teacher's tips

Don't get caught out when quantities are expressed in different units – convert them all to the same units before solving the problem.

Topic 6: Measures

Get started

The start (or prefix) of some measuring words can be helpful.

Start of word →	kilo	deci	centi	milli
Number link →	×1000	$\frac{1}{10}$	$\frac{1}{100}$	$\frac{1}{1000}$

1000 metres = 1 kilometre   10 decilitres = 1 litre   1000 kilogram = 1 tonne

10 decimetres = 1 metre   100 centilitres = 1 litre

100 centimetres = 1 metre   1000 millilitres = 1 litre   1000 grams = 1 kilogram

1000 millimetres = 1 metre

Practice

1 Write the missing numbers.

a ☐ cm = 1 metre   b ☐ mm = 1 centimetre   c ☐ m = 1 kilometre

d ☐ dm = 1 metre   e ☐ g = 1 kilogram   f ☐ kg = 1 tonne

g ☐ ml = 1 litre   h ☐ cl = 1 litre   i ☐ dl = 1 litre

j ☐ mm = 1 metre   k ☐ ml = 1 decilitre   l ☐ cl = 1 decilitre

2 Write each reading on the scales as kilograms like this: 2.5 kg

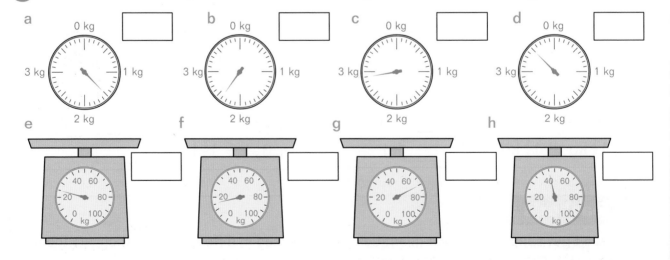

Challenge

3 Use a ruler that is marked in mm.

Measure the length of each of these lines to the nearest mm.

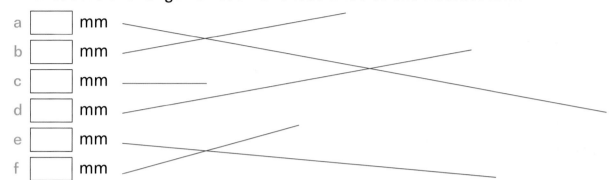

a [ ] mm

b [ ] mm

c [ ] mm

d [ ] mm

e [ ] mm

f [ ] mm

4 Use a ruler to measure the diameters these callipers have measured.

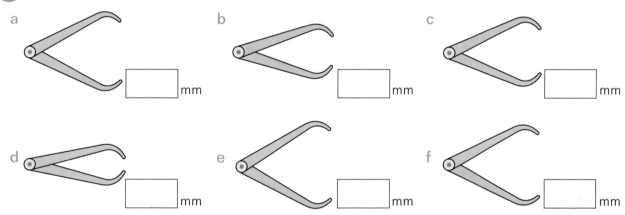

a [ ] mm

b [ ] mm

c [ ] mm

d [ ] mm

e [ ] mm

f [ ] mm

5 Here are some imperial measuring units.

Find out what each is worth in metric units.

> Remember the sign ≈ means approximately or nearly
>
> **1.9 m ≈ 2 m**

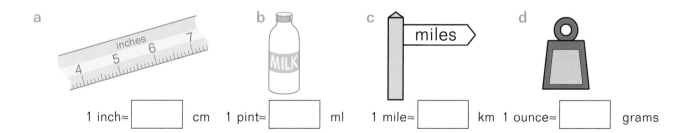

a 1 inch ≈ [ ] cm

b 1 pint ≈ [ ] ml

c 1 mile ≈ [ ] km

d 1 ounce ≈ [ ] grams

Teacher's tips

Imperial units are still used in many everyday situations, especially when shopping for groceries, so you need to know the approximate metric equivalent or you may find yourself with far more (or less) shopping than you expected!

Test 1 (Score 1 mark for every correct answer)

Topic 1

1 Add 99 to the number.

472 ☐

2 Write the answer.

$81 - (19 + 9) =$ ☐

3 Write in the missing number.

$84 - 29 = 19 +$ ☐

4 Draw brackets to make this true.

$34 - 45 - 19 = 8$

Topic 2

5 Write in the missing two digits.

◯ $\times 9 = 5$ ◯

6 Write the answer.

$(8 \times 7) - (5 \times 5) =$ ☐

7 Three tickets cost £24.

What will two tickets cost? £ ☐

8 I double a number then add 9.
The answer is 25. ☐
What is my number?

Topic 3

9 Write in figures:
Twenty-eight and a half thousand.

_____

10 Write the value of the bold digit.

2**2**57 500 _____

11 Divide this number by 100.

46 800 _____

12 Divide this number by 100.

(30k) ☐

Topic 4

13 To which number does the arrow point?

–15 –10 –5 0 5 10 15 ☐

14 Write these in order, lowest first.
$-5, 0, 4, -8, 3, -10$

____ ____ ____ ____ ____ ____

15 The temperature rises by 5°C.

-10 -8 -6 -4 -2 0 2 4 6 8 °C 10

Write the new temperature. ☐ °C

16 The temperature is 3°C and falls by 8°C. What is it now? ☐ °C

Topic 5

17 Write this measurement using a decimal point.

1 kg and 20 g = ☐ kg

18 Write in order, starting with the smallest. 1.05 m $1\frac{1}{4}$ m 1.5 m 120 cm

_____ _____ _____ _____

19 Write the answer in kilograms.

3 kg − 400 g = ☐ kg

20 Write the answer in litres.

Double 750 ml = ☐ l

Topic 6

21 Write the missing number.

$\frac{1}{2}$ cm = ☐ mm

22 What is the reading?

☐ kg

23 Measure this line to the nearest mm. _____ mm

_____

24 How many decilitres are in $\frac{1}{2}$ litre?

_____ dl

Mark the test. Remember to fill in your score on page 3.

Write your score out of 24. ☐

Add a bonus point if you scored 20 or more.

TOTAL SCORE FOR TEST 1 ☐

Topic 7: Fractions

Get started

Fractions have a **numerator** and a **denominator**.

$$\frac{4}{5}$$ ←**numerator**
←**denominator**

An improper fraction has a numerator that is larger than the denominator.

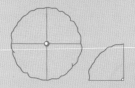

Here are five-quarters or $\frac{5}{4}$ of a pie

Improper fractions are greater than 1.

Practice

1 Write these as improper fractions.

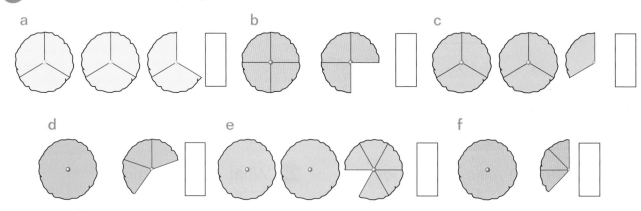

a

b

c

d

e

f

2 Write the answers.

a How many halves?	b How many thirds?	c How many eighths?	d How many tenths?
3 → ☐	2 → ☐	5 → ☐	4 → ☐
$2\frac{1}{2}$ → ☐	$1\frac{1}{3}$ → ☐	$2\frac{1}{8}$ → ☐	$1\frac{1}{10}$ → ☐
$4\frac{1}{2}$ → ☐	$3\frac{1}{3}$ → ☐	$3\frac{3}{8}$ → ☐	$1\frac{7}{10}$ → ☐
$1\frac{1}{2}$ → ☐	$2\frac{2}{3}$ → ☐	$1\frac{7}{8}$ → ☐	$3\frac{3}{10}$ → ☐

3 Change the whole numbers and proper fractions to improper fractions.

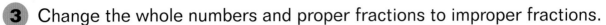
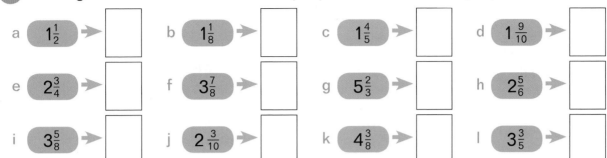

a $1\frac{1}{2}$ → ☐ b $1\frac{1}{8}$ → ☐ c $1\frac{4}{5}$ → ☐ d $1\frac{9}{10}$ → ☐

e $2\frac{3}{4}$ → ☐ f $3\frac{7}{8}$ → ☐ g $5\frac{2}{3}$ → ☐ h $2\frac{5}{6}$ → ☐

i $3\frac{5}{8}$ → ☐ j $2\frac{3}{10}$ → ☐ k $4\frac{3}{8}$ → ☐ l $3\frac{3}{5}$ → ☐

4 Change the improper fractions to whole numbers and proper fractions.

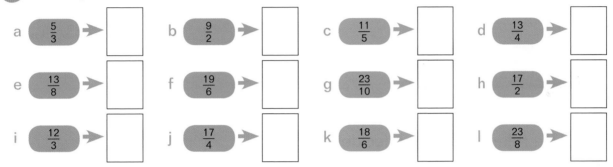

a $\frac{5}{3}$ → ☐ b $\frac{9}{2}$ → ☐ c $\frac{11}{5}$ → ☐ d $\frac{13}{4}$ → ☐

e $\frac{13}{8}$ → ☐ f $\frac{19}{6}$ → ☐ g $\frac{23}{10}$ → ☐ h $\frac{17}{2}$ → ☐

i $\frac{12}{3}$ → ☐ j $\frac{17}{4}$ → ☐ k $\frac{18}{6}$ → ☐ l $\frac{23}{8}$ → ☐

5 Write the shaded part as a whole number and a proper fraction.

The denominator should be as small as possible.

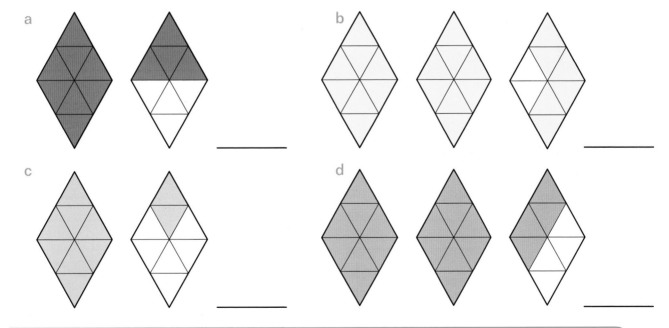

a _____ b _____

c _____ d _____

Teacher's tips

A quick way to calculate how to express a whole number as an improper fraction is to multiply the number of units by the denominator number, and then add the fractions of a whole unit. So $2\frac{1}{4}$ is $\frac{9}{4}$

Topic 8: 2D shapes

Get started

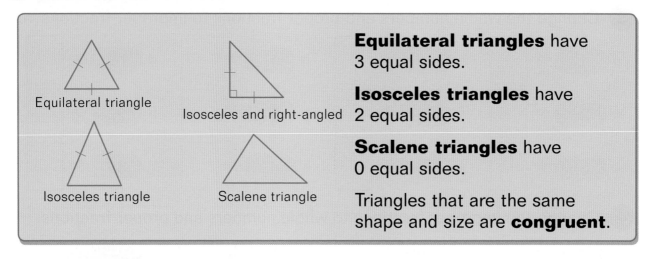

Equilateral triangles have 3 equal sides.

Isosceles triangles have 2 equal sides.

Scalene triangles have 0 equal sides.

Triangles that are the same shape and size are **congruent**.

Practice

1 Tick triangles that match the word.

Use a ruler to help you decide.

a Equilateral

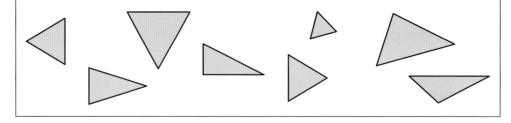

b Isosceles

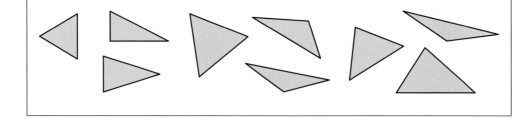

c Scalene

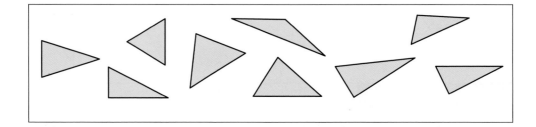

Challenge

2 Complete the table by ticking the correct word.

	A	B	C	D	E	F	G	H
Equilateral	✓							
Isosceles								
Scalene								

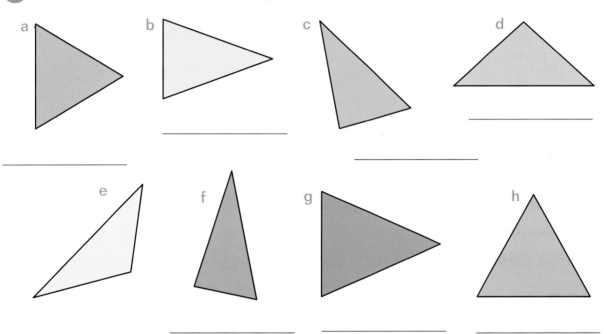

3 Write the name of each triangle.

a _____

b _____

c _____

d _____

e _____

f _____

g _____

h _____

4 Complete the table.

Write which triangles are the same shape and size as triangles X and Y.

Triangle	Congruent triangles
X	
Y	

Teacher's tips

If you see a small square drawn in a triangle, it means that angle is 90° (a right angle), and if you see single lines drawn through 2 sides of a triangle, it means those sides are the same length.

Topic 9: Time

Get started

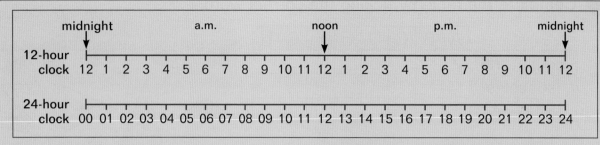

8.00 a.m. is written as 08:00   11.30 a.m. is written as 11:30
8.00 p.m. is written as 20:00   11.30 p.m. is written as 23:30

a.m. stands for ante meridiem and means in the morning
p.m. stands for post meridiem and means in the afternoon

A new day begins immediately after midnight.

23:59 is one minute   00:01 is one minute   12:00 is midday or noon
to midnight   after midnight

Practice

1 Write these times as 24-hour clock times.

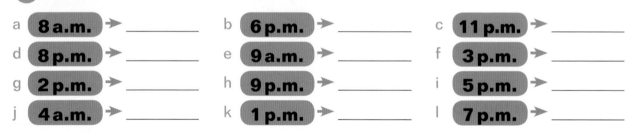

a **8 a.m.** → _____   b **6 p.m.** → _____   c **11 p.m.** → _____

d **8 p.m.** → _____   e **9 a.m.** → _____   f **3 p.m.** → _____

g **2 p.m.** → _____   h **9 p.m.** → _____   i **5 p.m.** → _____

j **4 a.m.** → _____   k **1 p.m.** → _____   l **7 p.m.** → _____

2 Write these as a.m. or p.m. times.

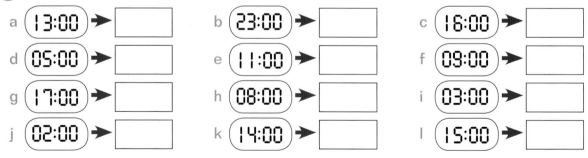

a 13:00 → [   ]   b 23:00 → [   ]   c 16:00 → [   ]

d 05:00 → [   ]   e 11:00 → [   ]   f 09:00 → [   ]

g 17:00 → [   ]   h 08:00 → [   ]   i 03:00 → [   ]

j 02:00 → [   ]   k 14:00 → [   ]   l 15:00 → [   ]

Challenge

3 Write these times as 24-hour clock times.

a	1.30 p.m.		b	8.45 a.m.		c	11.05 a.m.	
d	4.15 a.m.		e	9.55 p.m.		f	7.05 p.m.	
g	6.20 p.m.		h	5.50 p.m.		i	12 noon	
j	12.10 p.m.		k	1.35 a.m.		l	4.20 p.m.	

4 Write these as a.m. or p.m. times.

a (15:10) ➤

b (23:55) ➤

c (11:10) ➤

d (11:40) ➤

e (11:55) ➤

f (19:40) ➤

g (05:05) ➤

h (08:15) ➤

i (20:35) ➤

j (10:25) ➤

k (12:35) ➤

l (03:05) ➤

5 Write how many minutes are between each pair of times.

a | 08:15 | | 08:40 | _____

b | 10:05 | | 10:55 | _____

c | 12:25 | | 12:50 | _____

d | 16:20 | | 16:55 | _____

e | 11:55 | | 12:10 | _____

f | 14:35 | | 15:00 | _____

g | 21:45 | | 22:05 | _____

h | 23:50 | | 00:10 | _____

Teacher's tips

Digital time is written in a very similar way to decimal notation, but works differently because there are 60 minutes in an hour (and not 100) – don't get caught out!

Topic 10: Decimals

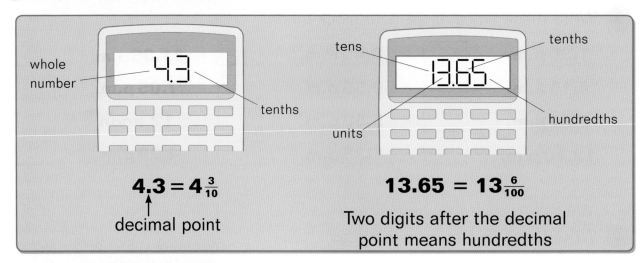

whole number → **4.3**   tenths

tens   units   tenths   hundredths

13.65

4.3 = 4 $\frac{3}{10}$

↑
decimal point

13.65 = 13 $\frac{6}{100}$

Two digits after the decimal point means hundredths

Practice

1 What is the digit 5 worth in each of these decimals?

a 15.8 → ☐   b 52.6 → ☐   c 8.5 → ☐   d 5.3 → ☐   e 0.5 → ☐

f 5.03 → ☐   g 7.05 → ☐   h 3.52 → ☐   i 25.06 → ☐   j 14.35 → ☐

2 Write these fractions as decimals.

a $\frac{7}{10}$ → ☐   b $\frac{3}{10}$ → ☐   c $\frac{9}{10}$ → ☐   d $\frac{45}{100}$ → ☐   e $\frac{75}{100}$ → ☐

f $1\frac{4}{10}$ → ☐   g $3\frac{9}{10}$ → ☐   h $5\frac{25}{100}$ → ☐   i $10\frac{65}{100}$ → ☐   j $\frac{5}{100}$ → ☐

3 Write each group of decimals in order, starting with the smallest.

a   0.6   0.4   0.7   0.1   0.3   0.9   0.5

b   1.3   0.9   1.4   1.1   1.8   1.9   1.6

_____   _____

Challenge

4 Round each decimal to the nearest whole number.

Remember to round up when the decimal part is 0.50 or more.

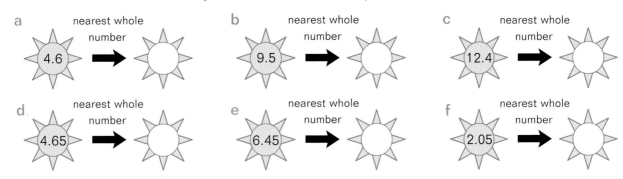

a nearest whole number 4.6 →

b nearest whole number 9.5 →

c nearest whole number 12.4 →

d nearest whole number 4.65 →

e nearest whole number 6.45 →

f nearest whole number 2.05 →

5 Write the decimal number each arrow points to.

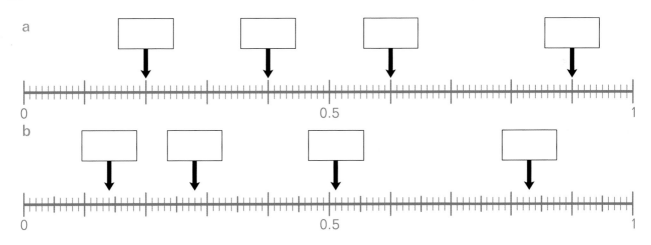

a

0   0.5   1

b

0   0.5   1

6 Rearrange each set of digits to make a decimal number as close to 5 as possible.

a (4)(6)(5)(.) ☐

b (3)(2)(8)(.) ☐

c (4)(9)(1)(.) ☐

d (8)(2)(0)(.) ☐

e (5)(6)(0)(.) ☐

f (4)(2)(7)(.) ☐

Teacher's tips

A decimal is a way of expressing a part of a unit, just like a fraction, except decimals always represent tenths, hundreds, thousands and so on.

Topic 11: Addition

Get started

Adding measurements and numbers that have a decimal point is quite like adding whole numbers.

Adding whole numbers	Adding money	Adding lengths	Adding decimals
4585 + 1307 5892 1	£45.85 + £13.07 £58.92 1	45.85 m + 13.07 m 58.92 m 1	45.85 + 13.07 58.92 1

Practice

1 Do these additions.

a　3558
+ 4672

b　1965
+ 2675

c　4077
+ 3659

d　1374
+ 4626

e　4466
+ 5178

f　£13.65
+ £18.75
£

g　£22.84
+ £12.65
£

h　£33.80
+ £26.74
£

i　£26.62
+ £19.17
£

j　£36.87
+ £44.76
£

k　13.75 m
+ 16.45 m

l　25.55 m
+ 37.25 m

m　27.84 m
+ 13.67 m

n　42.74 m
+ 65.18 m

o　42.25 m
+ 48.65 m

p　0.56 g
+ 0.75 g

q　5.87 g
+ 6.88 g

r　10.05 g
+ 11.58 g

s　22.64 g
+ 36.07 g

t　45.70 g
+ 16.56 g

2 Total these numbers and amounts.

a 〔56 m〕 〔128 m〕 〔89 m〕 ☐

b 〔£7.25〕 〔£1.74〕 〔£2.76〕 ☐

c 〔128 g〕 〔77 g〕 〔276 g〕 ☐

d 〔£0.83〕 〔£5.85〕 〔£9.27〕 ☐

e 〔1056〕 〔87〕 〔366〕 ☐

f 〔£6.62〕 〔£3.99〕 〔£5.24〕 ☐

g 〔376〕 〔3675〕 〔48〕 ☐

h 〔£0.76〕 〔£0.37〕 〔£2.83〕 ☐

Challenge

3 Write answers to the problems.

(4837) (2326) (1729) (5944) (3781)

a What is the total of all the even numbers in this set? _____

b What is the total of all the odd numbers in this set? _____

c What is the largest total that can be made by adding two of these numbers? _____

d Which three of the numbers have a total of 9999?

_____ _____ _____

4 Write in the missing digits.

a
```
    4 9 2 ◯
  + 3 ◯ 6 5
  ─────────
    7 9 8 6
```

b
```
  ◯ 3 1 5
  + 1 5 ◯ 2
  ─────────
    9 8 7 7
```

c
```
    4 8 2 9
  + 3 ◯ 5 ◯
  ─────────
    7 9 8 1
```

d
```
    6 2 1 ◯
  + 1 3 4 8
  ─────────
    7 ◯ 6 5
```

e
```
    6 2 5 ◯
  + 2 1 ◯ 6
  ─────────
    8 4 4 0
```

f
```
    4 ◯ 2 9
  + 2 7 ◯ 3
  ─────────
    7 0 2 2
```

g
```
    ◯ 7 1 8
  + 3 2 ◯ 2
  ─────────
    8 0 1 0
```

h
```
    3 9 0 ◯
  + 5 2 8 5
  ─────────
    9 1 9 0
```

5 Answer these problems.

a Four pairs of these numbers each total 5000.

Write the pairs. _____ _____

_____ _____

_____ _____

_____ _____

b Four pairs of these numbers each total 8000.

Write the pairs. _____ _____

_____ _____

_____ _____

_____ _____

(2792) (2614) (3281) (4212)

(4183) (1175) (3817) (1943)

(3825) (2208) (5179) (2386)

(1719) (3788) (6057) (2821)

Teacher's tips

When adding decimals you calculate the answer in the same way as whole numbers and, as with whole numbers, the position of the digit is critical in giving the number a value, so be careful to include the decimal point in the answer!

Topic 12: Subtraction

Get started

Subtracting money, measurements and numbers that have a decimal point is quite like subtracting whole numbers.

Subtracting whole numbers	Subtracting money	Subtracting lengths	Subtracting decimals
$$\begin{array}{r} {}^{5}\cancel{6}{}^{9}\cancel{0}{}^{1}4 \\ -\ 3\ 7\ 7 \\ \hline 2\ 2\ 7 \end{array}$$	$$\begin{array}{r} £{}^{5}\cancel{6}.{}^{9}\cancel{0}{}^{1}4 \\ -\ £3.7\ 7 \\ \hline £2.2\ 7 \end{array}$$	$$\begin{array}{r} {}^{5}\cancel{6}.{}^{9}\cancel{0}{}^{1}4\,m \\ -\ 3.7\ 7\,m \\ \hline 2.2\ 7 \end{array}$$	$$\begin{array}{r} {}^{5}\cancel{6}.{}^{9}\cancel{0}{}^{1}4 \\ -\ 3.7\ 7 \\ \hline 2.2\ 7 \end{array}$$

Remember you can check a subtraction by adding. **227 + 377 = 604**

Practice

1 Do these subtractions.

a
$$\begin{array}{r} 4\ 3\ 0 \\ -\ 1\ 7\ 4 \\ \hline \end{array}$$

b
$$\begin{array}{r} 6\ 1\ 2 \\ -\ 3\ 4\ 6 \\ \hline \end{array}$$

c
$$\begin{array}{r} 8\ 0\ 4 \\ -\ 1\ 6\ 5 \\ \hline \end{array}$$

d
$$\begin{array}{r} 6\ 0\ 3\ 4 \\ -\ 7\ 7\ 7 \\ \hline \end{array}$$

e
$$\begin{array}{r} 4\ 2\ 3\ 4 \\ -\ 1\ 5\ 5\ 4 \\ \hline \end{array}$$

f
$$\begin{array}{r} £2.5\ 6 \\ -\ £1.9\ 6 \\ \hline £ \end{array}$$

g
$$\begin{array}{r} £8.0\ 2 \\ -\ £4.1\ 4 \\ \hline £ \end{array}$$

h
$$\begin{array}{r} £9.1\ 0 \\ -\ £6.5\ 5 \\ \hline £ \end{array}$$

i
$$\begin{array}{r} £1\ 2.4\ 3 \\ -\ £\ \ 8.8\ 4 \\ \hline £ \end{array}$$

j
$$\begin{array}{r} £2\ 0.4\ 3 \\ -\ £1\ 3.6\ 8 \\ \hline £ \end{array}$$

k
$$\begin{array}{r} 5.23\ m \\ -\ 2.65\ m \\ \hline \end{array}$$

l
$$\begin{array}{r} 7.85\ m \\ -\ 0.65\ m \\ \hline \end{array}$$

m
$$\begin{array}{r} 7.16\ m \\ -\ 4.67\ m \\ \hline \end{array}$$

n
$$\begin{array}{r} 11.50\ m \\ -\ 5.86\ m \\ \hline \end{array}$$

o
$$\begin{array}{r} 1\ 5.67\ m \\ -\ 1\ 2.96\ m \\ \hline \end{array}$$

p
$$\begin{array}{r} 1.4\ 6 \\ -\ 0.8\ 9 \\ \hline \end{array}$$

q
$$\begin{array}{r} 7.2\ 3 \\ -\ 1.5\ 9 \\ \hline \end{array}$$

r
$$\begin{array}{r} 8.0\ 4 \\ -\ 4.0\ 8 \\ \hline \end{array}$$

s
$$\begin{array}{r} 1\ 0.0\ 6 \\ -\ 3.7\ 7 \\ \hline \end{array}$$

t
$$\begin{array}{r} 4\ 5.2\ 6 \\ -\ 2\ 2.6\ 8 \\ \hline \end{array}$$

2 Write the difference between each pair of numbers or amounts.

a (1205) (678) _____

b (£1.35) (£0.76) _____

c (88) (3006) _____

d (£4.50) (£2.77) _____

e (934) (87) _____

f (£10.20) (£3.28) _____

g (129) (5060) _____

h (£12.55) (£8.99) _____

28

Challenge

3 The diagram shows distances of some cities from London in kilometres.

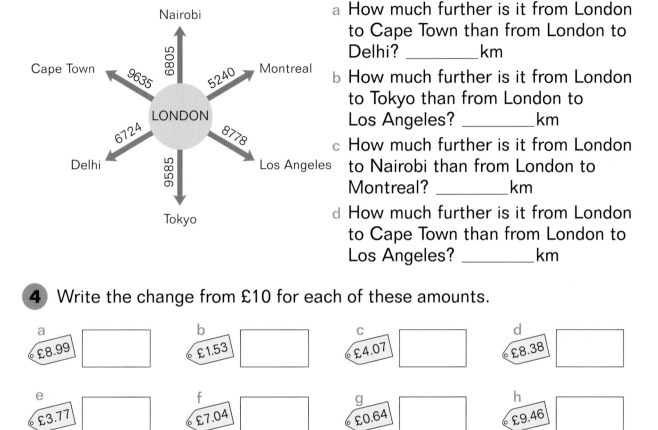

a How much further is it from London to Cape Town than from London to Delhi? _____ km

b How much further is it from London to Tokyo than from London to Los Angeles? _____ km

c How much further is it from London to Nairobi than from London to Montreal? _____ km

d How much further is it from London to Cape Town than from London to Los Angeles? _____ km

4 Write the change from £10 for each of these amounts.

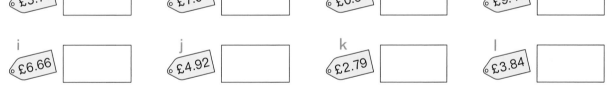

a £8.99

b £1.53

c £4.07

d £8.38

e £3.77

f £7.04

g £0.64

h £9.46

i £6.66

j £4.92

k £2.79

l £3.84

5 Join pairs of numbers that have a difference of 1299.

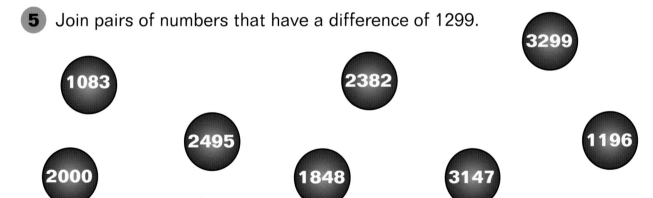

3299

1083

2382

2495

1196

2000

1848

3147

Teacher's tips

To calculate quickly the difference between two numbers simply subtract the smaller number from the bigger number.

Test 2 (Score 1 mark for every correct answer)

Topic 7

1 How many quarters are in $1\frac{1}{2}$?

$1\frac{1}{2} = $ ☐ quarters

2 Change to a whole number and a proper fraction.

$\frac{11}{4} = $ ☐

3 Change to an improper fraction.

$2\frac{5}{8} = $ ☐

4 Write as an improper fraction.

Topic 8

5 Tick the equilateral triangle.

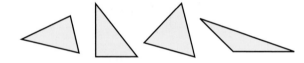

6 Tick the isosceles triangle.

7 Tick the scalene triangle.

8 Tick the right-angled isosceles triangle.

Topic 9

9 Write as an a.m. or p.m. time.

17:00 → ☐

10 Write as an a.m. or p.m. time.

11:55 → ☐

11 Write as a 24-hour clock time.

Six o'clock in the morning → ☐

12 Write as a 24-hour clock time.

Half past four in the afternoon → ☐

Topic 10

13 What is the bold digit worth?

23.**4**8 ☐

15 Write these decimals in order starting with the smallest.

0.25   0.5   0.75   0.95   0.4

_____ _____ _____ _____ _____

14 Round to the nearest whole number.

23.52 → ☐

16 To which decimal does the arrow point?

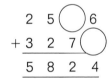

0   0.5   1.0

Topic 11

17 Add these decimals together.

4.7 and 8.35 ☐

19 Write the answer.

```
  8 4 5 6
      6 7 4
  +     7 6
  _____
```

18 What is the total of these amounts?

£7.56 and £13.59 _____

20 Write the missing digits.

```
    2  5 ◯ 6
  + 3  2  7 ◯
  _____
    5  8  2  4
```

Topic 12

21 Write the answer.

```
  8 0 6 0
 − 4 7 7 8
 _____
```

23 Subtract 4.66 from 12.25. ☐

22 If you cut 1.86 metres from 5 metres how much is left? ____ m

24 Write the change from £20.

£8.47   change → ☐

Mark the test. Remember to fill in your score on page 3.

Write your score out of 24.   ☐

Add a bonus point if you scored 20 or more.

TOTAL SCORE FOR TEST 2   ☐

Topic 13: Area and perimeter

Get started

The area of a rectangle or square is found by multiplying the **length** by the **breadth**.

6 cm

5 cm

Area = 6 cm × 5 cm
Area = 30 cm²

Area is measured in square units such as:

square centimetres cm²
square metres m²

Perimeter is the distance all the way round a shape.

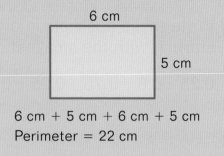

6 cm

5 cm

6 cm + 5 cm + 6 cm + 5 cm
Perimeter = 22 cm

Practice

1 Calculate the areas of these squares and rectangles.

a
8 cm
6 cm
Area = _____ cm²

b
12 cm
5 cm
Area = _____ cm²

c
9 cm
9 cm
Area = _____ cm²

d
15 cm
7 cm
Area = _____ cm²

e
12 cm
8 cm
Area = _____ cm²

f
7 cm
7 cm
Area = _____ cm²

2 Complete each table.

Rectangles		
Length	Breadth	Perimeter
8 cm	5 cm	
10 cm	9 cm	
12 cm	8 cm	
19 cm	12 cm	

Rectangles		
Length	Breadth	Perimeter
22 cm	15 cm	
17 cm	12 cm	
19 cm	18 cm	
25 cm	16 cm	

3 Measure the sides in centimetres.

Calculate the area and perimeter of each shape. It might help to divide each shape up into rectangles.

a

Area = _____ cm²
Perimeter = _____ cm

b

Area = _____ cm²
Perimeter = _____ cm

c

Area = _____ cm²
Perimeter = _____ cm

d

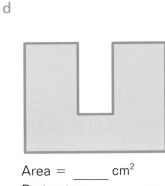

Area = _____ cm²
Perimeter = _____ cm

e

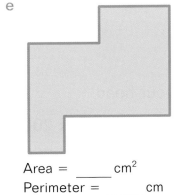

Area = _____ cm²
Perimeter = _____ cm

f

Area = _____ cm²
Perimeter = _____ cm

4 Calculate the area and perimeter of each letter.

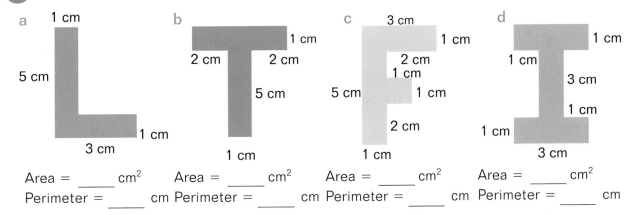

a   1 cm

5 cm

3 cm   1 cm

Area = _____ cm²
Perimeter = _____ cm

b   1 cm
2 cm   2 cm
5 cm

1 cm

Area = _____ cm²
Perimeter = _____ cm

c   3 cm
1 cm
2 cm
1 cm
5 cm   1 cm
2 cm
1 cm

Area = _____ cm²
Perimeter = _____ cm

d   1 cm
1 cm
3 cm
1 cm
1 cm
3 cm

Area = _____ cm²
Perimeter = _____ cm

Teacher's tips

Think of a *perimeter* fence, and a play *area*, to help you remember which is which. Remember to use the correct units for length and area – area is always the unit squared (e.g. cm²).

Topic 14: Short multiplication

Get started

There are different ways to multiply TU numbers.	**56 × 7 =** 50 × 7 = 350 6 × 7 = 42 56 × 7 = 392	5 6 × 7 $\overline{3\ 9\ 2}$ 4

There are many ways to multiply HTU numbers.

246 × 6 =
200 × 6 = 1200
40 × 6 = 240
6 × 6 = 36
246 × 6 = 1476

2 4 6
× 6
$\overline{1\ 4\ 7\ 6}$
2 3

Multiplying money is like multiplying numbers.   £2.46 × 6 = £14.76

Practice

1 Try to answer these in your head.

a 40 × 6 = _____   b 20 × 6 = _____   c 200 × 3 = _____   d 500 × 3 = _____

50 × 9 = _____   30 × 9 = _____   300 × 5 = _____   900 × 5 = _____

80 × 8 = _____   40 × 8 = _____   400 × 9 = _____   600 × 9 = _____

20 × 4 = _____   50 × 4 = _____   500 × 6 = _____   200 × 6 = _____

90 × 5 = _____   60 × 5 = _____   600 × 2 = _____   400 × 2 = _____

50 × 3 = _____   70 × 3 = _____   700 × 8 = _____   300 × 8 = _____

2 Calculate the answers to these using your own method.

a 34 × 6 = _____   b 120 × 4 = _____   c 224 × 7 = _____

d 55 × 3 = _____   e 250 × 5 = _____   f 174 × 5 = _____

g 85 × 8 = _____   h 620 × 5 = _____   i 623 × 5 = _____

j 72 × 9 = _____   k 750 × 3 = _____   l 506 × 9 = _____

m 26 × 8 = _____   n 910 × 6 = _____   o 629 × 3 = _____

p 47 × 7 = _____   q 480 × 8 = _____   r 732 × 4 = _____

s 99 × 3 = _____   t 330 × 6 = _____   u 927 × 8 = _____

v 65 × 7 = _____   w 360 × 9 = _____   x 748 × 2 = _____

Challenge

3 Use your own way to work out the answers to these problems.

a Which apple has the answer nearest to 500? Tick it.	88 × 9	67 × 8	92 × 6	63 × 9	73 × 9
b Which apple has the largest answer? Tick it.	74 × 4	87 × 3	38 × 7	65 × 4	58 × 5
c Which apples will have even answers? Tick them.	37 × 5	23 × 8	68 × 4	46 × 9	41 × 7
d Which apples will have odd answers? Tick them.	53 × 9	71 × 8	55 × 5	97 × 3	93 × 8

4 Complete these bills. (@ means 'at' e.g. 5 items at £2.36 each)

a 5 @ £2.36 = _____   b 6 @ £7.99 = _____

c 8 @ £4.77 = _____   d 8 @ £7.23 = _____

e 4 @ £7.25 = _____   f 5 @ £5.88 = _____

g 6 @ £6.92 = _____   h 7 @ £3.86 = _____

i 9 @ £7.37 = _____   j 3 @ £9.96 = _____

5 Join numbers into pairs.

One number must be twice the other.

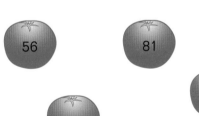
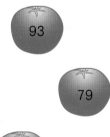

56   81   93

28   79

48   186   96

46   162   23   158

Teacher's tips

Break down larger numbers, or round to the nearest ten, to make short multiplication easier. If you round to ten remember to adjust your answer correctly.

Topic 15: 3D shapes

Get started

Prisms

triangular prism   pentagonal prism   octagonal prism

Pyramids

   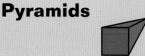

triangular pyramid or tetrahedron   square-based pyramid

pentagonal pyramid   hexagonal pyramid

The shape of the **ends** gives each prism its name.

Slices of a prism are all the same shape and size.

Cuboids and cubes are special types of prisms.

The shape of the **base** gives each pyramid its name.

The triangular faces of a pyramid all meet at a point.

A tetrahedron is a special pyramid, with a triangular base as well as triangular sides.

Practice

1 Name each of these prisms.

a   b   c 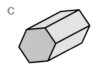   d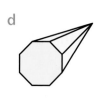

_____   _____   _____   _____

2 Name each of these pyramids.

a 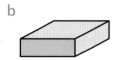   b   c   d

_____   _____   _____   _____

3 Tick all the tetrahedra.

Challenge

4 Sort the shapes into pyramids and prisms.

Complete the table by ticking the correct name.

	a	b	c	d	e	f	g	h
Prisms								
Pyramids								

a   b    c    d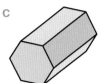

e 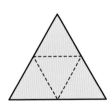   f 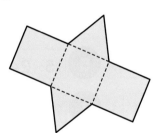   g 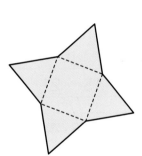   h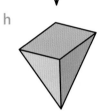

5 Write which shapes have been opened out flat to make these nets.

a   b   c   d

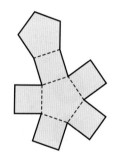

_____   _____   _____   _____

_____

6 Draw prisms starting from these shapes.

7 Draw pyramids starting from these shapes.

Topic 16: Special numbers

Get started

- **Multiples** are like the answers to multiplication tables.
  Multiples of 5 are 5, 10, 15, 20 ... **Multiples of 7** are 7, 14, 21, 28 ...
  Multiples go on and on. They do not stop at the tenth multiple.
  The **100th multiple** of 5 is 500   The **200th multiple** of 7 is 1400

- **Factors** divide exactly into a number.
  Factors of 12 in order are   **Factors of 12** in pairs are
  1, 2, 3, 4, 6, 12   (1, 12) (2, 6) (3, 4)

  Some numbers only have two **factors**. The **factors of 13** are (1,13).
  Numbers like this are called **prime numbers**. 13 is a prime number.
  1 is **not** a prime number because it has only one factor, not two.

- **Square numbers** are made when two identical whole numbers are
  multiplied together: $3 \times 3 = 9$ so 9 is a **square number**.
  Another way of writing 3×3 is 3^2 so $3^2 = 9$.

Practice

1 Ring all the numbers that are multiples of the blue number.

a **3** | 6   8   12   15   21   30   36

b **5** | 15   24   40   50   72   90   94   100

c **4** | 13   16   20   36   38   44   80   100

d **7** | 12   21   32   42   56   72   84   100

e **8** | 12   20   32   40   56   72   86   94

f **9** | 27   46   54   72   99   101   126   180

g **25** | 50 90 100 115 125 140 175 200

h **50** | 100 120 180 200 250 370 175 600

2 Write the factors of the start number in order, starting with the smallest.

a **6**

b **18**

c **24**

d **17**

e **21**

f **30**

g **16**

h **25**

i **36**

Challenge

3 Draw a ring round all the prime numbers.

> 6   17   11   9   19   3
>   5   2   12   18   7   13   24

4 Answer these questions about square numbers.

a What is 2 squared? ☐   b 3^2 = ☐   c ☐ × ☐ = 16

What is 4 squared? ☐ 5^2 = ☐   ☐ × ☐ = 36

What is 7 squared? ☐ 6^2 = ☐   ☐ × ☐ = 49

What is 8 squared? ☐ 9^2 = ☐   ☐ × ☐ = 64

What is 12 squared? ☐ 11^2 = ☐   ☐ × ☐ = 100

5 Answer the questions about these numbers.

> 18   36   49   56   72
> 16   24   45   54   70

a Which are square numbers?   b Which are multiples of 8?

_____   _____

c Which are multiples of both 4 and 6?   d Which are multiples of both 3 and 8?

_____   _____

6 Write the numbers 1 to 24 in the correct spaces on this Carroll diagram.

	prime number	not a prime number	
			factor of 24
			not factor of 24

Teacher's tips

Prime numbers help across many areas of Maths (and Science!) so they're worth learning. For instance, when simplifying fractions where the denominator or numerator is a prime number, can they be simplified further?

Topic 17: Division

Get started

There are different ways to divide numbers.

$78 \div 4$

$$4\overline{)78}$$
$$\underline{-40} \quad 4 \times 10$$
$$38$$
$$\underline{-36} \quad 4 \times 9$$
$$2 \quad \text{remainder}$$
$$= 19 \text{ r } 2$$

$$4\overline{)7^38} \quad \text{19 r 2}$$

Some divisions have a remainder.

quotient   remainder

19 r 2

$$4\overline{)78}$$

divisor

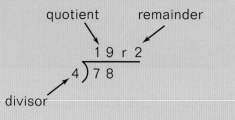

Practice

1 Try to answer these in your head.

Write the quotients.

a $20 \div 2 = \underline{10}$ b $120 \div 4 = \underline{30}$ c $180 \div 6 = \underline{30}$ d $240 \div 4 = \underline{}$

$40 \div 2 = \underline{20}$ $180 \div 2 = \underline{90}$ $720 \div 8 = \underline{90}$ $210 \div 3 = \underline{}$

$60 \div 2 = \underline{30}$ $240 \div 3 = \underline{80}$ $420 \div 7 = \underline{60}$ $320 \div 8 = \underline{}$

$80 \div 2 = \underline{40}$ $150 \div 5 = \underline{30}$ $630 \div 9 = \underline{70}$ $270 \div 3 = \underline{}$

$30 \div 2 = \underline{15}$ $320 \div 4 = \underline{80}$ $560 \div 8 = \underline{}$ $480 \div 6 = \underline{}$

$50 \div 2 = \underline{25}$ $450 \div 5 = \underline{90}$ $360 \div 6 = \underline{}$ $490 \div 7 = \underline{}$

$70 \div 2 = \underline{35}$ $210 \div 3 = \underline{70}$ $490 \div 7 = \underline{}$ $400 \div 5 = \underline{}$

$90 \div 2 = \underline{45}$ $360 \div 4 = \underline{90}$ $810 \div 9 = \underline{}$ $560 \div 8 = \underline{}$

2 Calculate the answers to these using your own method.

a $84 \div 2 = \underline{}$ b $96 \div 3 = \underline{}$ c $96 \div 4 = \underline{}$

d $88 \div 5 = \underline{}$ e $78 \div 7 = \underline{}$ f $90 \div 6 = \underline{}$

g $87 \div 8 = \underline{}$ h $66 \div 4 = \underline{}$ i $168 \div 4 = \underline{}$

j $475 \div 5 = \underline{}$ k $318 \div 2 = \underline{}$ l $252 \div 6 = \underline{}$

m $711 \div 9 = \underline{}$ n $408 \div 8 = \underline{}$ o $371 \div 7 = \underline{}$

p $744 \div 3 = \underline{}$ q $674 \div 5 = \underline{}$ r $832 \div 9 = \underline{}$

s $470 \div 7 = \underline{}$ t $887 \div 6 = \underline{}$ u $629 \div 8 = \underline{}$

v $907 \div 4 = \underline{}$ w $967 \div 9 = \underline{}$ x $568 \div 7 = \underline{}$

Challenge

3 Do these divisions.

a
$$4)\overline{9\ 5}$$

b
$$2)\overline{1\ 5\ 9}$$

c
$$8)\overline{5\ 8\ 3}$$

d
$$5)\overline{9\ 7\ 5}$$

e
$$5)\overline{8\ 7}$$

f
$$6)\overline{7\ 2\ 7}$$

g
$$6)\overline{7\ 3\ 8}$$

h
$$6)\overline{7\ 3\ 9}$$

i
$$3)\overline{7\ 8}$$

j
$$5)\overline{9\ 9\ 9}$$

k
$$7)\overline{8\ 8\ 2}$$

l
$$5)\overline{8\ 8\ 8}$$

m
$$6)\overline{9\ 1}$$

n
$$8)\overline{4\ 7\ 7}$$

o
$$3)\overline{8\ 0\ 5}$$

p
$$4)\overline{7\ 0\ 1}$$

4 An egg box holds 6 eggs. How many boxes are needed for each of these quantities? Some may not be full!

a (573 eggs) [ ]   b (314 eggs) [ ]   c (749 eggs) [ ]

d (204 eggs) [ ]   e (627 eggs) [ ]   f (319 eggs) [ ]

5 Look at the numbers then answer the problems.

a Which of the numbers are exactly divisible by 5? _____

b Which of the numbers has a remainder of 1 when the divisor is 4? _____

c Which of the numbers have 6 as a factor? _____

d Which of the numbers have a remainder of 2 when divided by 3? _____

e Which of the numbers is exactly divisible by 25? _____

667 **116** **780** **425** **762**

6 Work out the value of the missing digit.

a
$$6)\overline{3\ 9\ \bigcirc}\quad 6\ 5\ r\ 3$$

b
$$5)\overline{4\ 9\ \bigcirc}\quad 9\ 8\ r\ 3$$

c
$$9)\overline{7\ 6\ \bigcirc}\quad 8\ 4\ r\ 7$$

d
$$9)\overline{6\ 5\ \bigcirc}\quad 7\ 2\ r\ 2$$

Teacher's tips

Knowing your times tables is vital for quick and accurate division because division is just 'undoing' multiplication, so get learning those tables!

Topic 18: Lines and angles

Get started

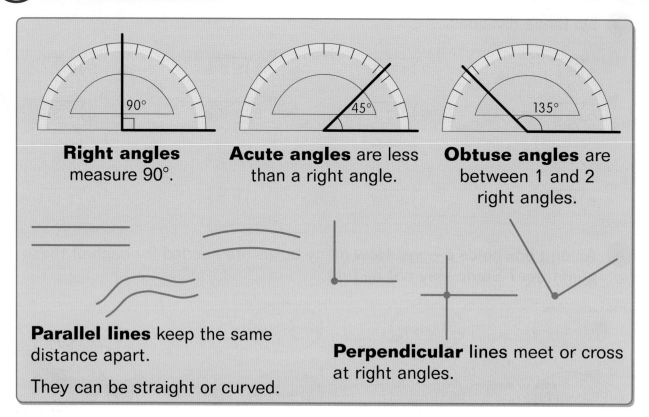

Right angles measure 90°.

Acute angles are less than a right angle.

Obtuse angles are between 1 and 2 right angles.

Parallel lines keep the same distance apart.

They can be straight or curved.

Perpendicular lines meet or cross at right angles.

Practice

1 Draw lines that are:

  a parallel with each of these   b perpendicular to each of these.

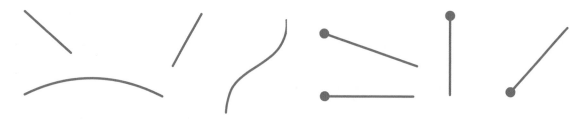

2 Write whether each angle is acute, obtuse or a right angle.

a   b   c   d   e   f   g

3 Look at the angles inside each of these shapes.

a Tick all the acute angles. b Tick all the obtuse angles. c Tick all the right angles.

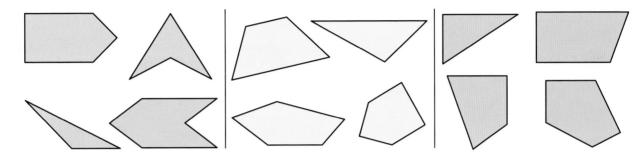

4 Look at the sides of these shapes.

Mark the parallel sides with little arrows like this:

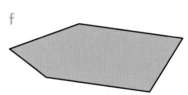

a

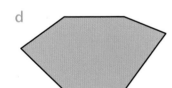

b

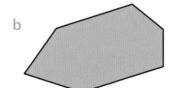

c

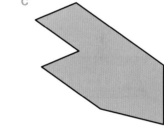

d

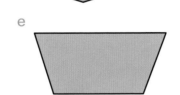

e

f

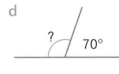

5 Calculate the size of each missing angle.

a

130° ?

_____

b

40° ?

_____

c

? 60°

_____

d

? 70°

_____

e

? 160°

_____

f

? 85°

_____

g

20° ?

_____

h

? 30°

_____

Teacher's tips

Knowing key facts about angles means you can calculate lots of unknown facts without having to measure. There are 360° in a full turn, 180° in a half-turn or straight line, and 90° in a quarter-turn or right angle.

Test 3 (Score 1 mark for every correct answer)

Topic 13

1 What is the area of a rectangle that measures 12 cm × 8 cm?

[   ] cm²

2 What is the perimeter of a square that has sides of 15 cm? [   ] cm

3 Calculate the area of this shape.

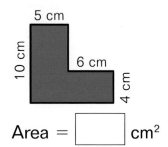

5 cm
10 cm
6 cm
4 cm

Area = [   ] cm²

4 Calculate the perimeter of this shape.

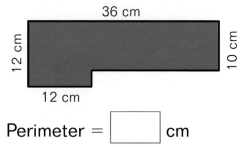

36 cm
12 cm
10 cm
12 cm

Perimeter = [   ] cm

Topic 14

5 74 × 7 = [   ]

6
```
  3 5 6
×     4
-------
```

7 What is double £8.89? [   ]

8 Write the missing digit.
```
      9○
×      6
-------
  5 4 6
```

Topic 15

9 Name this shape.

_____

10 Name this shape.

_____

11 Cross the odd one out.

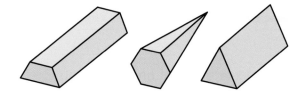

12 Which of these is a square based pyramid opened out?

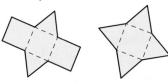

Tick the right shape.

Topic 16

13 Ring all the numbers that are multiples of 6.

21 30 42 46 50 56 72

14 Write all the factors of 40.

Start with the smallest.

15 Ring all the numbers that are prime numbers.

2 4 6 9 11 13 21

16 What is 12 squared?

Topic 17

17 $89 \div 3 =$ _____

18 $6 \overline{) 8 \ 3 \ 4}$

19 A car can carry 4 people.

How many cars are needed

for 39 people? ☐ cars

20 Divide 235 by 9.

Quotient = ☐

Remainder = ☐

Topic 18

21 Tick lines that are perpendicular.

22 Tick lines that are parallel.

23 Tick the obtuse angles.

24 Tick the acute angles.

Mark the test. Remember to fill in your score on page 3.

Write your score out of 24.

Add a bonus point if you scored 20 or more.

TOTAL SCORE FOR TEST 3

Topic 19: Handling data

Get started

Graphs have two **axes**.

There is a **horizontal axis** and a **vertical axis**.

The axes have **labels** that give you information.

Numbered axes should always have a **scale**.

Graphs can have bars, columns or lines.

The lines on line graphs can be straight, broken or curved.

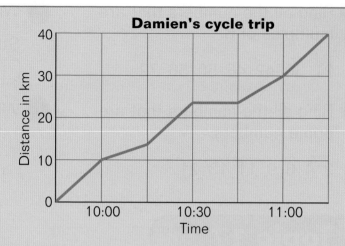

Damien's cycle trip

The **mode** is the value that occurs most often.

The **range** is the difference between the highest and lowest values.

Here are some scores:
13 15 15 16 16 16 16 17 17 19 19 19 23

The mode is 16
The range is (23 − 13) = 10

Practice

1 Answer the questions about this bar graph.

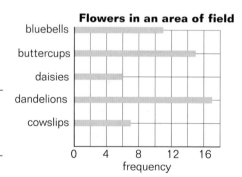

Flowers in an area of field

a Which flower was the most common? _____

b Which flower was the least common? _____

c Which plant occurred 15 times? _____

d How many dandelions were there? _____

e What is the range? _____

f How many plants were counted altogether? _____

Challenge

2 a Between which times did the temperature remain the same?

Between _____ and _____

b Between which two times did the temperature rise the most?

Between _____ and _____

c Between which times was the temperature less than 17°C?

Between _____ and _____

d What was the temperature range?

_____

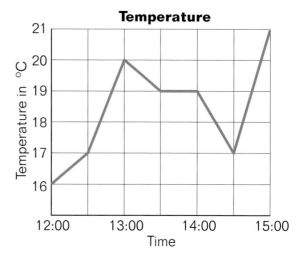

Temperature

3 a When did the baby weigh 3 kg? _____

b When did the baby weigh 4.5 kg?

_____

c When did the baby lose weight?

Between weeks _____ and _____

d About how heavy was the baby at 7 weeks? _____

e When was the baby 3.25 kg?

Between weeks _____ and _____

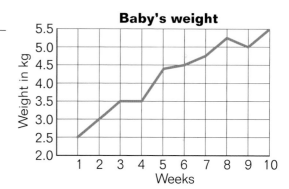

Baby's weight

4 This is about an experiment on same-sized pieces of fabric.

a What was the dry weight of fabric C?

_____

b What was the wet weight of fabric D?

_____

c What was the difference between the wet and dry weights of fabric A? _____

d Which fabrics absorbed the most water? _____

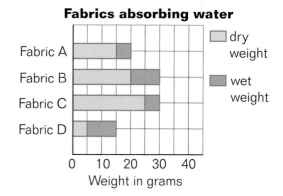

Fabrics absorbing water

Teacher's tips

Always read the labels and scale on a graph very carefully – they can look similar but be very different and therefore give very different information.

Topic 20: Fractions of numbers

Get started

What is $\frac{1}{4}$ of 120?	**What is $\frac{3}{4}$ of 64?**
To find $\frac{1}{4}$ of an amount divide by 4.	$\frac{1}{4}$ of 64 is 16
$\frac{1}{4}$ of 120 is 30	$\frac{3}{4}$ of 64 is 48

You divide by the denominator then multiply by the numerator.

Practice

1 Write the answers.

Try to answer as many as you can in your head.

a $\frac{1}{5}$ of 35 = ☐ b $\frac{1}{2}$ of 18 = ☐ c $\frac{1}{4}$ of 36 = ☐ d $\frac{1}{7}$ of 42 = ☐

e $\frac{1}{5}$ of 75 = ☐ f $\frac{1}{2}$ of 48 = ☐ g $\frac{1}{3}$ of 96 = ☐ h $\frac{1}{4}$ of 92 = ☐

i $\frac{1}{10}$ of 450 = ☐ j $\frac{1}{8}$ of 240 = ☐ k $\frac{1}{8}$ of 560 = ☐ l $\frac{1}{7}$ of 350 = ☐

m $\frac{1}{3}$ of 600 = ☐ n $\frac{1}{10}$ of 700 = ☐ o $\frac{1}{2}$ of 500 = ☐ p $\frac{1}{5}$ of 900 = ☐

2 Work out the answers to these.

Try to answer them in your head.

a $\frac{2}{3}$ of 21 = ☐ b $\frac{3}{4}$ of 16 = ☐ c $\frac{2}{5}$ of 25 = ☐ d $\frac{3}{8}$ of 24 = ☐

e $\frac{3}{10}$ of 50 = ☐ f $\frac{5}{8}$ of 32 = ☐ g $\frac{2}{3}$ of 30 = ☐ h $\frac{7}{10}$ of 40 = ☐

i $\frac{3}{4}$ of 120 = ☐ j $\frac{2}{3}$ of 270 = ☐ k $\frac{4}{5}$ of 250 = ☐ l $\frac{3}{8}$ of 160 = ☐

m $\frac{7}{10}$ of 200 = ☐ n $\frac{7}{8}$ of 400 = ☐ o $\frac{3}{5}$ of 200 = ☐ p $\frac{9}{10}$ of 800 = ☐

Challenge

3 Write the answers.

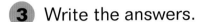

39p   15 litres   45 g   £2.10   63 cm

a What is $\frac{2}{3}$ of these? _____ _____ _____ _____ _____

95 cm   £4.50   35 litres   65 g   75p

b What is $\frac{4}{5}$ of these? _____ _____ _____ _____ _____

42 g   60p   48 ml   72 cm   £1.20

c What is $\frac{5}{6}$ of these? _____ _____ _____ _____ _____

4 Calculate these answers.

a What is $\frac{3}{4}$ of these?

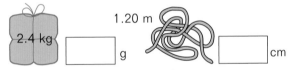

2.4 kg [   ] g   1.20 m [   ] cm   1.6 litres [   ] ml

b What is $\frac{3}{10}$ of these?

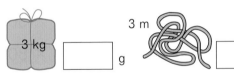 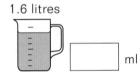 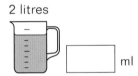

3 kg [   ] g   3 m [   ] cm   2 litres [   ] ml

5 What is $\frac{3}{4}$ of these lengths?

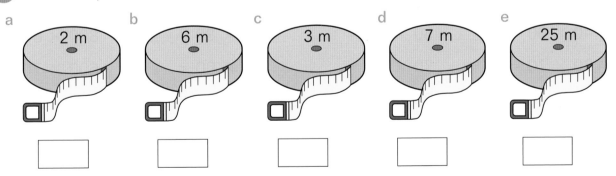

a   b   c   d   e

2 m   6 m   3 m   7 m   25 m

[   ]   [   ]   [   ]   [   ]   [   ]

Teacher's tips

Practise the order for solving calculations involving fractions of numbers or quantities – first divide by the denominator, and then multiply by the numerator.

Get started

Multiplying by multiples of 10 and 100

Multiply the non-zero digits first, then adjust for the zeros.

30 × 70 = 2100
700 × 80 = **56**000

The most common mistake is to get the number of zeros wrong.

Multiplying 2-digit numbers together

Here are two ways of calculating 26 × 48.

	40	**8**
20	800	160
6	240	48

```
     2 6
   × 4 8
  1 0 4 0  26 × 40
    2 0 8  26 × 8
  1 2 4 8
```

The total is 1248

Always do a quick estimate to check:
26 × 48 ≃ 30 × 50 = 1500

Practice

1 Try to answer these in your head.

a 30 × 80 = _____   b 50 × 50 = _____   c 200 × 50 = _____   d 900 × 80 = _____

50 × 70 = _____   40 × 80 = _____   300 × 80 = _____   500 × 90 = _____

70 × 70 = _____   30 × 30 = _____   500 × 30 = _____   500 × 60 = _____

20 × 90 = _____   80 × 90 = _____   600 × 90 = _____   600 × 50 = _____

80 × 60 = _____   20 × 60 = _____   200 × 60 = _____   700 × 30 = _____

40 × 60 = _____   50 × 80 = _____   400 × 80 = _____   800 × 80 = _____

30 × 70 = _____   70 × 60 = _____   100 × 60 = _____   600 × 70 = _____

80 × 80 = _____   90 × 90 = _____   400 × 90 = _____   900 × 90 = _____

2 Complete these tables.

a

×40	
24	
36	
44	
57	

b

×60	
28	
45	
63	
72	

c

×70	
38	
59	
76	
88	

Challenge

3 Calculate the answers to these.

a
```
   2 5
×  3 9
───────
```

b
```
   3 6
×  3 6
───────
```

c
```
   5 2
×  6 8
───────
```

d
```
   5 6
×  9 1
───────
```

e
```
   3 6
×  2 6
───────
```

f
```
   2 8
×  4 5
───────
```

g
```
   6 4
×  7 8
───────
```

h
```
   7 5
×  3 5
───────
```

i
```
   2 7
×  2 8
───────
```

j
```
   4 6
×  5 8
───────
```

k
```
   8 9
×  2 6
───────
```

l
```
   2 8
×  9 7
───────
```

m
```
   3 6
×  2 3
───────
```

n
```
   5 2
×  3 6
───────
```

o
```
   7 7
×  3 8
───────
```

p
```
   5 3
×  7 4
───────
```

4 Calculate the area of each rectangle.

a
37 cm
28 cm
_____ cm²

b
46 cm
34 cm
_____ cm²

c
64 cm
49 cm
_____ cm²

d
59 cm
45 cm
_____ cm²

e
71 cm
58 cm
_____ cm²

5 Answer these problems.

a An egg tray holds 12 eggs. How many eggs will 24 trays hold? _____

b A gallon is about 4.5 litres. Approximately how many litres is 10 gallons? _____

c Tickets cost £26 each. What will be the total cost of 16 tickets? _____

d A DVD disc holds 4.7 Gb of information. How many Gb will 20 discs hold? _____

e A box weighs 13 kg. What would be the total weight of 16 boxes? _____

f An inch is about 2.5 cm. Approximately how long is 36 inches in cm? _____

Teacher's tips

Choose the method that you find most logical and then practise that method, making lots of notes to show your working so any mistakes can be corrected easily.

Topic 22: Equivalent fractions

Get started

Equivalent fractions have different numerators and denominators but are worth the same.

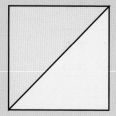 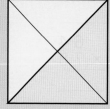

$\frac{1}{2}$ and $\frac{2}{4}$ are equivalent fractions.

You can reduce a fraction to an equivalent fraction by **cancelling**.

To cancel you divide top and bottom by the same number.

$$\frac{8 \div 4}{12 \div 4} = \frac{2}{3}$$

Practice

1 Complete these equivalent fractions.

a  $\frac{1}{2} = \frac{}{8}$

b 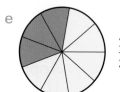 $\frac{1}{4} = \frac{}{16}$

c 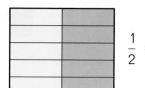 $\frac{1}{2} = \frac{}{10}$

d  $\frac{3}{4} = \frac{}{16}$

e 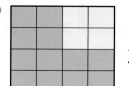 $\frac{2}{3} = \frac{}{9}$

f  $\frac{3}{4} = \frac{}{8}$

2 Complete these equivalent fractions.

a  $\frac{}{10} = \frac{}{5}$

b  $\frac{}{12} = \frac{3}{}$

c  $\frac{}{7} = \frac{2}{}$

d $\frac{4}{} = \frac{}{3}$

e $\frac{3}{} = \frac{}{8}$

f  $\frac{}{9} = \frac{2}{}$

52

Challenge

3 Complete the equivalent fractions.

a $\dfrac{1}{2} = \dfrac{}{12}$ b $\dfrac{1}{2} = \dfrac{}{10}$ c $\dfrac{1}{2} = \dfrac{}{18}$ d $\dfrac{1}{2} = \dfrac{}{30}$ e $\dfrac{1}{2} = \dfrac{}{100}$

f $\dfrac{1}{3} = \dfrac{}{12}$ g $\dfrac{1}{4} = \dfrac{}{20}$ h $\dfrac{1}{5} = \dfrac{}{30}$ i $\dfrac{1}{8} = \dfrac{}{24}$ j $\dfrac{1}{10} = \dfrac{}{100}$

k $\dfrac{1}{3} = \dfrac{4}{}$ l $\dfrac{1}{5} = \dfrac{5}{}$ m $\dfrac{1}{8} = \dfrac{3}{}$ n $\dfrac{1}{6} = \dfrac{5}{}$ o $\dfrac{1}{10} = \dfrac{7}{}$

4 Cancel each fraction so that you have the smallest possible denominator.

a $\dfrac{12}{16} = \boxed{}$ b $\dfrac{8}{24} = \boxed{}$ c $\dfrac{15}{18} = \boxed{}$ d $\dfrac{40}{100} = \boxed{}$ e $\dfrac{5}{20} = \boxed{}$

f $\dfrac{16}{24} = \boxed{}$ g $\dfrac{9}{15} = \boxed{}$ h $\dfrac{28}{32} = \boxed{}$ i $\dfrac{25}{100} = \boxed{}$ j $\dfrac{14}{16} = \boxed{}$

5 Cross out the mistake in each set.

a

$\dfrac{2}{20}$	$\dfrac{6}{60}$	$\dfrac{20}{200}$
$\dfrac{2}{5}$	$\dfrac{3}{30}$	$\dfrac{10}{100}$

equivalent to $\dfrac{1}{10}$

b

$\dfrac{24}{30}$	$\dfrac{40}{50}$	$\dfrac{100}{125}$
$\dfrac{16}{20}$	$\dfrac{8}{10}$	$\dfrac{20}{20}$

equivalent to $\dfrac{4}{5}$

c

$\dfrac{6}{16}$	$\dfrac{12}{32}$	$\dfrac{21}{56}$
$\dfrac{30}{80}$	$\dfrac{9}{18}$	$\dfrac{27}{72}$

equivalent to $\dfrac{3}{8}$

Teacher's tips

Fractions are normally written in their simplest form. However, to do calculations with fractions we may need to change them, so they have a common (same) denominator, by writing equivalent fractions – before simplifying the answer.

Get started

Percentages are hundredths.

The percentage sign is %.

$30\% = \frac{30}{100}$

Common percentages are:

$10\% = \frac{10}{100} = \frac{1}{10}$

$50\% = \frac{50}{100} = \frac{1}{2}$

$25\% = \frac{25}{100} = \frac{1}{4}$

$75\% = \frac{75}{100} = \frac{3}{4}$

Percentages must be out of 100.

$\frac{3}{10} = \frac{30}{100} = 30\%$

$\frac{4}{5} = \frac{60}{100} = 80\%$

Here are some percentages of money.

| 1% of £1 = 1p | 10% of £1 = 10p | 25% of £1 = 25p | 50% of £1 = 50p |

Practice

1 Write these as percentages.

a 40 out of 100   b 70 out of 100   c 25 out of 100   d 45 out of 100   e 85 out of 100

_____   _____   _____   _____   _____

f 7 out of 10   g 3 out of 10   h 9 out of 10   i 5 out of 10   j 6 out of 10

_____   _____   _____   _____   _____

2 Write these fractions as percentages.

a $\frac{15}{100}$ ▸ _____   b $\frac{35}{100}$ ▸ _____   c $\frac{95}{100}$ ▸ _____   d $\frac{17}{100}$ ▸ _____   e $\frac{8}{100}$ ▸ _____

f $\frac{8}{10}$ ▸ _____   g $\frac{1}{2}$ ▸ _____   h $\frac{1}{4}$ ▸ _____   i $\frac{3}{4}$ ▸ _____   j $\frac{1}{5}$ ▸ _____

3 Write the percentage of each square that is shaded.

a 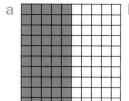   b 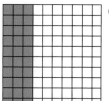   c 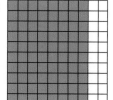   d 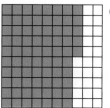   e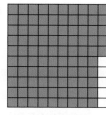

_____ %   _____ %   _____ %   _____ %   _____ %

Challenge

4 Write these percentages as fractions in their lowest terms.

a 20%

b 50%

c 80%

d 25%

e 75%

_____   _____   _____   _____   _____

5 Work out these percentages.

a What is 10% of these amounts?

£1   £2   £5   £20   £100   £150   £300   £750

_____ _____ _____ _____ _____ _____ _____ _____

b What is 20% of these amounts?

£1   £3   £5   £15   £20   £50   £75   £120

_____ _____ _____ _____ _____ _____ _____ _____

c What is 50% of these amounts?

£1   £2   £4   £7   £25   £70   £150   £500

_____ _____ _____ _____ _____ _____ _____ _____

6 Write the percentage of each shape that is shaded.

a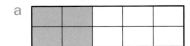

b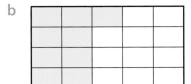

c

_____ %   _____ %   _____ %

Topic 24: Symmetry

Get started

Lines of symmetry are like mirror lines. One half is the reflection of the other half.

Lines of symmetry are not always horizontal or vertical.

Some shapes have no lines of symmetry – others have one or more.

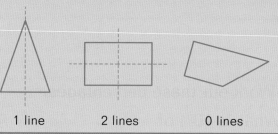

1 line   2 lines   0 lines

Practice

1 Draw all the lines of symmetry on these shapes.

a 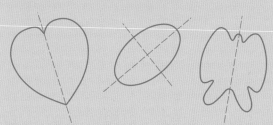 b c d

e   f   g   h

2 Draw the missing half of these symmetrical shapes.

a 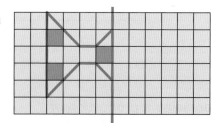   b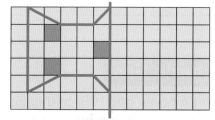

3 Draw the reflection of each shape to the right of the mirror line.

a
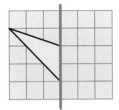

b
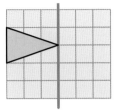

c
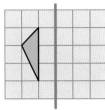

d
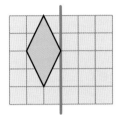

e
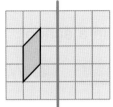

f
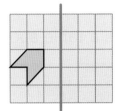

4 Tick all the true sentences for these shapes.

They are all right-angled.

They are all quadrilaterals.

They all have at least one line of symmetry.

5 Draw freehand the reflections of these shapes.

a
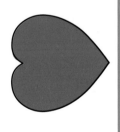

mirror line

b
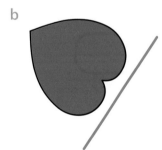

mirror line

Teacher's tips

Imagine the shape is a piece of paper – if you can fold the paper in half so both sides are exactly the same then the shape is symmetrical and the 'fold' is the line of symmetry.

Test 4 (Score 1 mark for every correct answer)

Topic 19

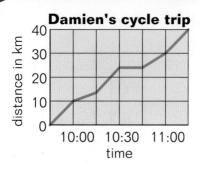

Damien's cycle trip

1 For how long did Damien stop cycling? _____

2 How far did he travel between 10:00 and 10:45? _____

Here is a table about class sizes in a school.

Class	1	2	3	4	5	6	7
Number of children	29	27	33	29	30	31	29

3 What is the range? _____

4 What is the mode? _____

Topic 20

5 What is $\frac{1}{8}$ of £120? _____

6 What is $\frac{1}{10}$ of £3.50? _____

7 What is $\frac{3}{5}$ of 120 km? _____

8 What is $\frac{3}{4}$ of 3.60 metres? _____

Topic 21

9 Write the answer.

$60^2 = $ ☐

10 Work out the answer.

$58 \times 80 = $ _____

11 Calculate the answer.

$$\begin{array}{r} 6\,4 \\ \times\ 4\,7 \\ \hline \\ \hline \end{array}$$

12 Calculate the area of the square.

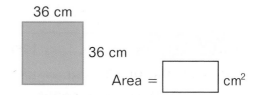

36 cm

36 cm

Area = ☐ cm²

Topic 22

13 Write the fraction that is shaded.

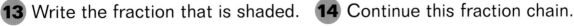

⬜⬜⬜⬜/⬜⬜ or ⬜/⬜

14 Continue this fraction chain.

$$\frac{1}{4} = \frac{2}{8} = \frac{3}{-} = \frac{}{-} = \frac{}{-}$$

15 Cancel this fraction. $\frac{16}{20} = \frac{}{-}$

16 Write an equivalent fraction. $\frac{10}{15} = \frac{2}{-}$

Topic 23

17 Write the fraction as a percentage.

$\frac{7}{10}$ ➡ ⬜ %

18 Write this percentage as a fraction.

20% ➡ ⬜

19 What is 20% of £5? ⬜

20 How much is shaded?

 ⬜ %

Topic 24

21 Draw in all the lines of symmetry.

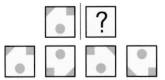

22 Which have no line of symmetry.?

23 Tick the missing reflection.

24 Draw the reflection of the letter.

E |
mirror

Mark the test. Now add up all your test scores and put your final score on page 3.

Write your score out of 24. ⬜

Add a bonus point if you scored 20 or more.

TOTAL SCORE FOR TEST 4 ⬜

Answers

Topic 1: Mental maths (page 4)

1.
a. 15	b. 21	c. 80	d. 76	e. 366
8	27	140	82	672
18	64	80	108	798
8	64	100	84	574
18	71	150	73	963
13	73	90	78	688
13	83	160	63	373
6	36	110	55	765

2.
a. 86	b. 141	c. 366	d. 36
95	146	697	17
136	356	63	27
137	367	27	227

3.
a. 57	b. 81	c. 45	d. 65
63	71	56	78
35	64	81	83

4.
a.	27	43
b.	27	65
c.	8	82
d.	32	51
e.	23	52
f.	45	64
g.	15	16
h.	44	12
i.	35	36

5.
a. out	23	34	52	69	88
b. out	97	123	140	166	171
c. in	53	65	73	81	86
d. in	32	82	108	143	218

6.
a. $16 - (4 + 6) = 6$ b. $(20 - 9) + 4 = 15$
c. $(17 - 3) + 7 = 21$ d. $22 - (9 + 1) = 12$
e. $13 - (7 - 2) = 8$ f. $18 - (10 - 3) = 11$
g. $(20 - 8) - 4 = 8$ h. $(21 - 10) - 3 = 8$

Topic 2: Tables (page 6)

1.
a. 30	b. 36	c. 6	d. 7	e. 44
49	54	5	7	77
72	72	6	3	99
12	80	4	6	33
21	18	5	7	88
45	48	5	8	48
40	28	7	3	60
0	32	7	10	72

2.
a. 9   b. 49   c. 45
d. 6   e. 9   f. 8
g. 37   h. 41   i. 41
j. 28   k. 54   l. 78

3.
a.
×	4	6	8
3	12	18	24
7	28	42	56
9	36	54	72

c.
×	3	5	8
9	27	45	72
11	33	55	88
12	36	60	96

b.
×	3	5	9
4	12	20	36
6	18	30	54
7	21	35	63

d.
×	3	5	9
5	15	25	45
8	24	40	72
9	27	45	81

4.
Other answers are possible.
a. 2×12 3×8
b. 3×10 5×6
c. 9×4 3×12
d. 2×9 3×6
e. 4×10 5×8
f. 6×8 4×12
g. 6×10 5×12
h. 9×8 6×12
i. 10×10 20×5

5.
a. £42
b. £12
c. 60p
d. 24p
e. £32
f. 54p
g. £72
h. £72

6.
a. 9
b. 8
c. 30
d. 8

Topic 3: Place value (page 8)

1.
a. 24 000
b. 2 000 000
c. 340 000
d. 1 200 000
e. 6409
f. 5 050 000
g. 200 000
h. 6 000 075
i. 15 007
j. 9 001 002

2.
a. 50 000   b. 5000
c. 90 000   d. 700
e. 500   f. 600 000
g. 2 000 000   h. 500 000
i. 50 000   j. 5000
k. 1 000 000   l. 70 000

3.
a. 60 000   g. 800
b. 120 000   h. 1300
c. 300 000   i. 5000
d. 900 000   j. 40
e. 1 500 000   k. 220
f. 7 000 000   l. 400

4.
a. 6500
b. 500 000
c. 12 500
d. 250 000
e. 22 500
f. 750 000
g. 162 500
h. 1 750 000
i. 5250
j. 9 250 000

5.
a. 5000
b. 50 000
c. 25 000
d. 750
e. 7500
f. 60 000

Topic 4: Negative numbers (page 10)

1.
a. −5
b. −10
c. −8
d. 2
e. −11
f. 8

2.
a. −3   0
b. −7   −6
c. −4   −2
d. −3   0
e. −12   −4
f. −45   −35

3.
a. −8   −5   0   4   6
b. −9   −3   −1   4   5
c. −50   −45   −20   0   10
d. −67   −32   −11   17   25

4.
a. 3°C
b. −7°C
c. −2°C
d. −5°C
e. 6°C

5.
a. 7°C
b. 10°C
c. 9°C
d. 10°C
e. 7°C

6.
a. −2
b. −5
c. −5
d. −6

Topic 5: Decimal points (page 12)

1.
a. 2.7 l   b. 1.2 kg   c. 2.1 km
d. 5.05 l   e. 3.03 kg   f. 1.04 km
g. 1.005 l   h. 2.005 kg   i. 5.005 km
j. 0.25 l   k. 0.75 kg   l. 0.5 km
m. 3.5 l   n. 6.5 kg   o. 4.5 km

2.
a. 2.8 m	b. 1.75 kg	c. 2.82 l	d. 8.5 km
550 cm	2250 g	1750 ml	3250 m
3.07 m	2.075 kg	1.075 l	5.06 km
20 cm	800 g	200 ml	100 m
6 m	0.75 kg	0.9 l	0.45 km

3.
a. 0.405 kg   450 g $\frac{1}{2}$ kg
b. 1025 g   1.200 kg $1\frac{1}{4}$ kg
c. 2570 g   2.705 kg $2\frac{3}{4}$ kg
d. 0.7 kg $\frac{3}{4}$ kg   800 g
e. 700 ml   0.705 l $\frac{3}{4}$ l
f. 1.125 l   1215 ml $1\frac{1}{4}$ l
g. 2.225 l $2\frac{1}{4}$ l   2550 ml
h. 1650 ml $1\frac{3}{4}$ l   1.8 l

4.
a. 46 kg
b. 2 kg
c. 2.750 kg
d. 5 l
e. 5 ml
f. 0.3 l

5.
a. 2.15 kg
b. 1.75 kg
c. 4.2 kg
d. 2.75 kg
e. 2.35 l
f. 4.875 l
g. 2.25 l
h. 4.75 l

Topic 6: Measures (page 14)

1.
a. 100 cm **b.** 10 mm **c.** 1000 m
d. 10 dm **e.** 1000 g **f.** 1000 kg
g. 1000 ml **h.** 100 cl **i.** 10 dl
j. 1000 mm **k.** 100 ml **l.** 10 cl

2.
a. 1.5 kg
b. 2.4 kg
c. 2.9 kg
d. 3.5 kg
e. 25 kg
f. 15 kg
g. 70 kg
h. 45 kg

3.
a. 135 mm
b. 62 mm
c. 23 mm
d. 97 mm
e. 103 mm
f. 50 mm

4.
a. 15 mm
b. 7 mm
c. 11 mm
d. 3 mm
e. 18 mm
f. 16 mm

5.
a. $2\frac{1}{2}$ cm
b. 600 ml
c. 1.6 km
d. 25 g

Test 1 (page 16)

1. 571
2. 53
3. 36
4. $34 - (45 - 19) = 8$
5. $6 \times 9 = 54$
6. 31
7. £16
8. 8
9. 28 500
10. 200 000
11. 468
12. 300
13. −11
14. −10 −8 −5 0 3 4
15. −3°C
16. −5°C
17. 1.02 kg
18. 1.05 m 120 cm $1\frac{1}{4}$ m 1.5 m
19. 2.6 kg
20. 1.5 l
21. 5 mm
22. 25 kg
23. 47 mm
24. 5 dl

Topic 7: Fractions (page 18)

1.
a. $\frac{8}{3}$
b. $\frac{7}{4}$
c. $\frac{7}{3}$
d. $\frac{8}{5}$
e. $\frac{17}{6}$
f. $\frac{11}{8}$

2.
a. 6   5   9   3
b. 6   4   10   8
c. 40   17   27   15
d. 40   11   17   33

3.
a. $\frac{3}{2}$
b. $\frac{9}{8}$
c. $\frac{9}{5}$
d. $\frac{19}{10}$
e. $\frac{11}{4}$
f. $\frac{31}{8}$
g. $\frac{17}{3}$
h. $\frac{17}{6}$
i. $\frac{29}{8}$
j. $\frac{23}{10}$
k. $\frac{35}{8}$
l. $\frac{18}{5}$

4.
a. $1\frac{2}{3}$
b. $4\frac{1}{2}$
c. $2\frac{1}{5}$
d. $3\frac{1}{4}$
e. $1\frac{5}{8}$
f. $3\frac{1}{6}$
g. $2\frac{3}{10}$
h. $8\frac{1}{2}$
i. 4
j. $4\frac{1}{4}$
k. 3
l. $2\frac{7}{8}$

5.
a. $1\frac{1}{2}$
b. $2\frac{3}{4}$
c. $1\frac{1}{4}$
d. $2\frac{1}{2}$

Topic 8: 2D shapes (page 20)

1.

a. Equilateral

b. Isosceles

c. Scalene
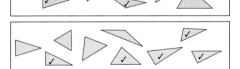

2.

	A	B	C	D	E	F	G	H
Equilateral	☑		☑					
Isosceles				☑		☑		☑
Scalene		☑		☑		☑	☑	

3.
a. equilateral
b. isosceles
c. scalene
d. isosceles
e. scalene
f. scalene
g. isosceles
h. equilateral

4.

Triangle	Congruent triangles
X	A, B, E
Y	F, H

Topic 9: Time (page 22)

1.
a. 08:00 **b.** 18:00 **c.** 23:00
d. 20:00 **e.** 09:00 **f.** 15:00
g. 14:00 **h.** 21:00 **i.** 17:00
j. 04:00 **k.** 13:00 **l.** 19:00

2.
a. 1.00 p.m. **b.** 11.00 p.m. **c.** 4.00 p.m.
d. 5.00 a.m. **e.** 11.00 a.m. **f.** 9.00 a.m.
g. 5.00 p.m. **h.** 8.00 a.m. **i.** 3.00 a.m.
j. 2.00 a.m. **k.** 2.00 p.m. **l.** 3.00 p.m.

3.
a. 13:30 **b.** 08:45 **c.** 11:05
d. 04:15 **e.** 21:55 **f.** 19:05
g. 18:20 **h.** 17:50 **i.** 12:00
j. 12:10 **k.** 01:35 **l.** 16:20

4.
a. 3.10 p.m. **b.** 11.55 p.m. **c.** 11.10 a.m.
d. 11.40 a.m. **e.** 11.55 a.m. **f.** 7.40 p.m.
g. 5.05 a.m. **h.** 8.15 a.m. **i.** 8.35 p.m.
j. 10.25 a.m. **k.** 12.35 p.m. **l.** 3.05 a.m.

5.
a. 25 minutes **b.** 50 minutes
c. 25 minutes **d.** 35 minutes
e. 15 minutes **f.** 25 minutes
g. 20 minutes **h.** 20 minutes

Topic 10: Decimals (page 24)

1.
a. 5 **b.** 50 **c.** $\frac{5}{10}$ **d.** 5 **e.** $\frac{5}{10}$
f. 5 **g.** $\frac{5}{100}$ **h.** $\frac{5}{10}$ **i.** 5 **j.** $\frac{5}{100}$

2.
a. 0.7 **b.** 0.3 **c.** 0.9 **d.** 0.45 **e.** 0.75
f. 1.4 **g.** 3.9 **h.** 5.25 **i.** 10.65 **j.** 0.05

3.
a. 0.1 0.3 0.4 0.5 0.6 0.7 0.9
b. 0.9 1.1 1.3 1.4 1.6 1.8 1.9

4.
a. 5 **b.** 10 **c.** 12
d. 5 **e.** 6 **f.** 2

5.
a. 0.2 0.4 0.6 0.9
b. 0.14 0.28 0.51 0.83

6.
a. 4.65 **b.** 3.82 **c.** 4.91
d. 2.80 **e.** 5.06 **f.** 4.72

Topic 11: Addition (page 26)

1.
a. 8230 b. 4640 c. 7736 d. 6000 e. 9644
f. £32.40 g. £35.49 h. £60.54 i. £45.79 j. £81.63
k. 30.2 m l. 62.8 m m. 41.51 m n. 107.92 m o. 90.9 m
p. 1.31 g q. 12.75 g r. 21.63 g s. 58.71 g t. 62.26 g

2.
a. 273 m b. £11.75 c. 481 g d. £15.95
e. 1509 f. £15.85 g. 4099 h. £3.96

3.
a. 8270 b. 10 347 c. 10 781 d. 2326 1729 5944

4.
a.
```
  4 9 2 (1)
+ 3 (0) 6 5
  7 9 8 6
```
b.
```
  (8) 3 1 5
+ 1 5 (6) 2
  9 8 7 7
```
c.
```
  4 8 2 9
+ 3 (1) 5 (2)
  7 9 8 1
```
d.
```
  6 2 1 (7)
+ 1 3 4 8
  7 (5) 6 5
```
e.
```
  6 2 5 (4)
+ 2 1 (8) 6
  8 4 4 0
```
f.
```
  4 (2) 2 9
+ 2 7 (9) 3
  7 0 2 2
```
g.
```
  (4) 7 1 8
+ 3 2 (9) 2
  8 0 1 0
```
h.
```
  3 9 0 (5)
+ 5 2 8 5
  9 1 9 0
```

5.
a. 2792 and 2208
2614 and 2386
3281 and 1719
1175 and 3825
b. 4212 and 3788
4183 and 3817
1943 and 6057
5179 and 2821

Topic 12: Subtraction (page 28)

1.
a. 256 b. 266 c. 639 d. 5257 e. 2680
f. £0.60 g. £3.88 h. £2.55 i. £3.59 j. £6.75
k. 2.58 m l. 7.2 m m. 2.49 m n. 5.64 m o. 2.71 m
p. 0.57 q. 5.64 r. 3.96 s. 6.29 t. 22.58

2.
a. 527 b. £0.59 c. 2918 d. £1.73
e. 847 f. £6.92 g. 4931 h. £3.56

3.
a. 2911 km b. 807 km c. 1565 km d. 857 km

4.
a. £1.01 b. £8.47 c. £5.93 d. £1.62
e. £6.23 f. £2.96 g. £9.36 h. £0.54
i. £3.34 j. £5.08 k. £7.21 l. £6.16

5.
1083 and 2382   2000 and 3299   2495 and 1196   1848 and 3147

Test 2 (page 30)

1. 6 **2.** $2\frac{3}{4}$ **3.** $\frac{21}{8}$ **4.** $\frac{19}{8}$

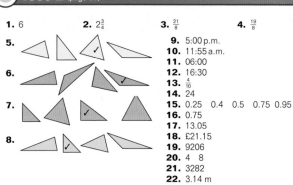

9. 5:00 p.m.
10. 11:55 a.m.
11. 06:00
12. 16:30
13. $\frac{4}{10}$
14. 24
15. 0.25 0.4 0.5 0.75 0.95
16. 0.75
17. 13.05
18. £21.15
19. 9206
20. 4 8
21. 3282
22. 3.14 m
23. 7.59
24. £11.53

Topic 13: Area and perimeter (page 32)

1.
a. 48 cm²
b. 60 cm²
c. 81 cm²
d. 105 cm²
e. 96 cm²
f. 49 cm²

2.
a. 26 cm b. 74 cm
   38 cm   58 cm
   40 cm   74 cm
   62 cm   82 cm

3.
a. area 11 cm²   perimeter 14 cm
b. area 7 cm²   perimeter 12 cm
c. area 6 cm²   perimeter 14 cm
d. area 10 cm²   perimeter 18 cm
e. area 11 cm²   perimeter 16 cm
f. area 11 cm²   perimeter 16 cm

4.
a. L area 7 cm² perimeter 16 cm b. T area 10 cm² perimeter 22 cm
c. F area 8 cm² perimeter 18 cm d. I area 9 cm² perimeter 20 cm

Topic 14: Short multiplication (page 34)

1.
a. 240	b. 120	c. 600	d. 1500
450	270	1500	4500
640	320	3600	5400
80	200	3000	1200
450	300	1200	800
150	210	5600	2400

2.
a. 204 b. 480 c. 1568
d. 165 e. 1250 f. 870
g. 680 h. 3100 i. 3115
j. 648 k. 2250 l. 4554
m. 208 n. 5460 o. 1887
p. 329 q. 3840 r. 2928
s. 297 t. 1980 u. 7416
v. 455 w. 3240 x. 1496

3.
a. 88 × 9 | 67 × 8 ✓ | 92 × 6 | 63 × 9 | 73 × 9
b. 74 × 4 ✓ | 87 × 3 | 38 × 7 | 65 × 4 | 58 × 5
c. 37 × 5 | 23 × 8 ✓ | 68 × 4 | 46 × 9 ✓ | 41 × 7
d. 53 × 9 ✓ | 71 × 8 | 55 × 5 ✓ | 97 × 3 ✓ | 93 × 8

4.
a. £11.80
b. £47.94
c. £38.16
d. £57.84
e. £29.00
f. £29.40
g. £41.52
h. £27.02
i. £66.33
j. £29.88

5.
48 and 96
23 and 46
93 and 186
81 and 162
28 and 56
79 and 158

Topic 15: 3D shapes (page 36)

1.
a. triangular prism
b. cuboid
c. hexagonal prism
d. octagonal prism

2.
a. square-based pyramid
b. triangular pyramid (or tetrahedron)
c. hexagonal pyramid
d. octagonal pyramid

3.

5.
a. triangular pyramid or tetrahedron
b. triangular prism
c. square-based pyramid
d. pentagonal prism

4.
	a	b	c	d	e	f	g	h
Prisms		✓	✓		✓	✓		
Pyramids	✓			✓			✓	✓

6. ▱ ▱ ▱   **7.** ◁ ▷ ◁ ▷

Topic 16: Special numbers (page 38)

1.
a. 6 12 15 21 30 36
b. 15 40 50 90 100
c. 16 20 36 44 80 100
d. 21 42 56 84
e. 32 40 56 72
f. 27 54 72 99 126 180
g. 50 100 125 175 200
h. 100 200 250 600

2.
a. 1 2 3 6
b. 1 2 3 6 9 18
c. 1 2 3 4 6 8 12 24
d. 1 17
e. 1 3 7 21
f. 1 2 3 5 6 10 15 30
g. 1 2 4 8 16
h. 1 5 25
i. 1 2 3 4 6 9 12 18 36

3.
5 17 2 11 7 19 13 3

4.
a.	4	b. 9	c. 4 × 4
	16	25	6 × 6
	49	36	7 × 7
	64	81	8 × 8
	144	121	10 × 10

5.
a. 16 36 49
b. 16 24 56 72
c. 24 36 72
d. 24 72

6.

prime number	not a prime number	
2	4 6	factor of 24
3	1 8 12	
	24	
5 11 7	9 10 14	not a factor of 24
13 17	15 16 18	
19 23	20 21 22	

Topic 17: Division (page 40)

1.
a.	10	b.	30	c.	30	d.	60
	20		90		90		70
	30		80		60		40
	40		30		70		90
	15		80		70		80
	25		90		60		70
	35		70		70		80
	45		90		90		70

2.
a. 42   **b.** 32   **c.** 24
d. 17 r 3   **e.** 11 r 1   **f.** 15
g. 10 r 7   **h.** 16 r 2   **i.** 42
j. 95   **k.** 159   **l.** 42
m. 79   **n.** 51   **o.** 53
p. 248   **q.** 134 r 4   **r.** 92 r 4
s. 67 r 1   **t.** 147 r 5   **u.** 78 r 5
v. 226 r 3   **w.** 107 r 4   **x.** 81 r 1

3.
a. 23 r 3 **b.** 79 r 1   **c.** 72 r 7 **d.** 195
e. 17 r 2 **f.** 121 r 1 **g.** 123   **h.** 123 r 1
i. 26   **j.** 199 r 4 **k.** 126   **l.** 177 r 3
m. 15 r 1 **n.** 59 r 5   **o.** 268 r 1 **p.** 175 r 1

4.
a. 96 **b.** 53   **c.** 125
d. 34 **e.** 105 **f.** 54

5.
a. 780 425
b. 425
c. 780 762
d. 116 425
e. 425

6.
a. 3
b. 3
c. 3
d. 0

Topic 18: Lines and angles (page 42)

1.
a.

b.

2.
a. acute
b. right angle
c. obtuse
d. right angle
e. acute
f. obtuse
g. right angle

3.
a. Acute angles **b.** Obtuse angles **c.** Right

4.
a.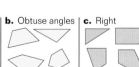
b.
c.
d.
e.
f.

5.
a. 50°
b. 140°
c. 120°
d. 110°
e. 20°
f. 95°
g. 160°
h. 150°

Test 3 (page 44)

1. 96 cm²   **2.** 60 cm
3. 74 cm²   **4.** 96 cm
5. 518   **6.** 1424
7. £17.78   **8.** 1
9. hexagonal pyramid   **10.** hexagonal prism
11.

12.

13. 30 42 72   **14.** 1 2 4 5 8 10 20 40
15. 2 11 13   **16.** 144
17. 29 r 2   **18.** 139
19. 10   **20.** 26 r 1
21.   **22.**

23.   **24.**

Topic 19: Handling data (page 46)

1.
a. dandelion
b. daisy
c. buttercup
d. 17
e. 11
f. 56

2.
a. 13:30 and 14:00
b. 14:30 and 15:00
c. 12:00 and 12:30
d. 5°C

3.
a. week 2
b. week 6
c. weeks 8 and 9
d. 4.75 kg
e. weeks 2 and 3

4.
a. 25 g
b. 15 g
c. 5 g
d. B and D

Topic 20: Fractions of numbers (page 48)

1.
a. 7   **b.** 9   **c.** 9   **d.** 6
e. 15   **f.** 24   **g.** 32   **h.** 23
i. 45   **j.** 30   **k.** 70   **l.** 50
m. 200   **n.** 70   **o.** 250   **p.** 180

2.
a. 14   **b.** 12   **c.** 10   **d.** 9
e. 15   **f.** 20   **g.** 20   **h.** 28
i. 90   **j.** 180   **k.** 200   **l.** 60
m. 140   **n.** 350   **o.** 120   **p.** 720

3.
a. 26p   10 l   30 g   £1.40   42 cm
b. 76 cm   £3.60   28 l   52 g   60p
c. 35 g   50p   40 ml   60 cm   £1.00

4.
a. 1800 g   90 cm   1200 ml   **b.** 900 g   90 cm   600 ml

5.
a. 1.5 m   **b.** 4.5 m   **c.** 2.25 m   **d.** 5.25 m   **e.** 18.75 m

Topic 21: Long multiplication (page 50)

1.
a.	2400	b.	2500	c.	10 000	d.	72 000
	3500		3200		24 000		45 000
	4900		900		15 000		30 000
	1800		7200		54 000		30 000
	4800		1200		12 000		21 000
	2400		4000		32 000		64 000
	2100		4200		6 000		42 000
	6400		8100		36 000		81 000

2.
a.	960	b.	1680	c.	2660
	1440		2700		4130
	1760		3780		5320
	2280		4320		6160

3.
a. 975   **b.** 1296 **c.** 3536 **d.** 5096
e. 936   **f.** 1260 **g.** 4992 **h.** 2625
i. 756   **j.** 2668 **k.** 2314 **l.** 2716
m. 828   **n.** 1872 **o.** 2926 **p.** 3922

4.
a. 1036 cm²
b. 1564 cm²
c. 3136 cm²
d. 2655 cm²
e. 4118 cm²

5.
a. 288 eggs   **b.** 45 litres
c. £416   **d.** 94 Gb
e. 208 kg   **f.** 90 cm

Topic 22: Equivalent fractions (page 52)

1.
a. $\frac{4}{8}$ **b.** $\frac{4}{16}$ **c.** $\frac{5}{10}$
d. $\frac{12}{16}$ **e.** $\frac{6}{9}$ **f.** $\frac{6}{8}$

2.
a. $\frac{6}{10} = \frac{3}{5}$ **b.** $\frac{9}{12} = \frac{3}{4}$ **c.** $\frac{1}{7} = \frac{2}{14}$
d. $\frac{4}{6} = \frac{2}{3}$ **e.** $\frac{3}{4} = \frac{6}{8}$ **f.** $\frac{6}{9} = \frac{2}{3}$

3.
a. 6 **b.** 5 **c.** 9 **d.** 15 **e.** 50
f. 4 **g.** 5 **h.** 6 **i.** 3 **j.** 10
k. 12 **l.** 25 **m.** 24 **n.** 30 **o.** 70

4.
a. $\frac{3}{4}$ **b.** $\frac{1}{3}$ **c.** $\frac{5}{6}$ **d.** $\frac{2}{5}$ **e.** $\frac{1}{4}$
f. $\frac{2}{3}$ **g.** $\frac{3}{5}$ **h.** $\frac{7}{8}$ **i.** $\frac{1}{4}$ **j.** $\frac{7}{8}$

5.
a. $\frac{2}{5}$ **b.** $\frac{20}{20}$ **c.** $\frac{9}{18}$

Topic 23: Percentages (page 54)

1.
a. 40% **b.** 70% **c.** 25% **d.** 45%
e. 85% **f.** 70% **g.** 30% **h.** 90%
i. 50% **j.** 60%

2.
a. 15% **b.** 35% **c.** 95% **d.** 17%
e. 8% **f.** 80% **g.** 50% **h.** 25%
i. 75% **j.** 20%

3.
a. 50% **b.** 30% **c.** 80% **d.** 75% **e.** 95%

4.
a. $\frac{1}{5}$ **b.** $\frac{1}{2}$ **c.** $\frac{4}{5}$ **d.** $\frac{1}{4}$ **e.** $\frac{3}{4}$

5.
a. 10p 20p 50p £2 £10 £15 £30 £75
b. 20p 60p £1 £3 £4 £10 £15 £24
c. 50p £1 £2 £3.50 £12.50 £35 £75 £250

6.
a. 40%
b. 45%
c. 40%

Topic 24: Symmetry (page 56)

1.
a. 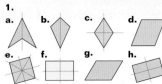 **b.** **c.** **d.**
e. 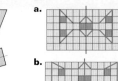 **f.** **g.** **h.**

2.
a.

b.

3.
a. **b.** **c.**
d. 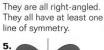 **e.** **f.**

4.
They are all right-angled.
They all have at least one
line of symmetry.

5.
a.
mirror line

b.
mirror line

Test 4 (page 58)

1. 15 min
2. 15 km
3. 6
4. 29
5. 15
6. 35p
7. 72 km
8. 2.7 m
9. 3600
10. 4640
11. 3008
12. 1296 cm²
13. $\frac{9}{12}$ or $\frac{3}{4}$
14. $\frac{3}{12}$ $\frac{4}{16}$ $\frac{5}{20}$
15. $\frac{16}{20} = \frac{4}{5}$
16. $\frac{10}{15} = \frac{2}{3}$
17. 70%
18. $\frac{1}{5}$
19. £1
20. 75%

21.

22.

23.

24.
mirror